Growing Up with Good Food is [...] families. It provides ideas and recipe[...] just for babies and young children. [...] should be enjoyed as part of family l[...] Attitudes to food and good nutrition[...] to generation and it is vital to devel[...] young children. Parents and children are, t[...] encouraged to have fun cooking together where the child will quickly absorb the parent's attitude to food and its preparation.

The book aims to make the reader more conscious of nutritional matters. It will help parents become more independent as cooks, able to adapt basic recipes and it encourages a more adventurous spirit in the kitchen. There is material on a good diet for pregnant and breastfeeding mothers, as well as on the preparation of baby foods. Recipes for vegetarian and non-vegetarian families are included and *Growing Up with Good Food* also deals with cakes, biscuits, preserves and party-treats with suggestions on limiting the intake of sweets.

Written for parents by parents, *Growing Up with Good Food* grew out of the desire of the Leeds Branch of The National Childbirth Trust for a sensible book on the virtues of good food for the whole family. Catherine Lewis, mother of two children, was brought up on good food – everything homemade and homegrown – and was encouraged to 'help' in the kitchen from an early age.

GROWING UP WITH GOOD FOOD

Edited by **CATHERINE LEWIS**

Foreword by **Penelope Leach**

Published in association with The National Childbirth Trust

London
UNWIN PAPERBACKS
Boston   Sydney

This edition published by Unwin Paperbacks 1984
First published by Unwin Paperbacks 1982
First published by The National Childbirth Trust 1978

UNWIN® PAPERBACKS
40 Museum Street, London WC1A 1LU, UK

Unwin Paperbacks
Park Lane, Hemel Hempstead, Herts HP2 4TE, UK

George Allen & Unwin Australia Pty Ltd
8 Napier Street, North Sydney, NSW 2060, Australia

British Library Cataloguing in Publication Data

Growing up with good food.
1. Cookery
I. Lewis, Catherine   II. National Childbirth Trust
641.5   TX705
ISBN 0–04–641046 5

Set in 9 on 10 point Times by Bedford Typesetters Ltd,
and printed in Great Britain
by The Guernsey Press Co. Ltd, Guernsey, Channel Islands

Publisher's Note

Originally published by the Leeds Branch of The National Childbirth Trust on a local basis, *Growing Up with Good Food* proved so popular that this revised and expanded paperback edition has been created to meet a widely felt need among parents. The Technical Committee of the NCT has approved it and royalties will go to support the work of the Trust nationally. Although care has been taken to ensure that the text is well informed and the advice given sound, the book should not be taken to represent NCT policy on diet. Any correspondence concerning the book should be addressed to Catherine Lewis, 2 Headingley Terrace, Leeds LS6 2EE, UK.

THE NATIONAL CHILDBIRTH TRUST

The National Childbirth Trust is a registered charity which aims to help women to have their babies happily and without fear, and to prepare young families for the experience of childbirth and parenthood. NCT antenatal classes teach methods of breathing and relaxation which help a woman cope with labour and build confidence in both parents through group discussion. For women who wish to breastfeed, the Breastfeeding Promotion Group offers mother-to-mother help through its breastfeeding counsellors. In many areas informal post-natal groups are open to new parents who wish to talk with other new parents on a shared self-help basis.

For further information, please write to the NCT, 9 Queensborough Terrace, Bayswater, London W2 3TB, or telephone 01-221 3833.

Acknowledgements

So many people contributed to *Growing Up with Good Food* – whether by inspiring the idea in the first place, or helping with the preparation, production and publication of the Leeds edition, or, through its distribution, enabling the book to prove itself a success with thousands of families – that we can only thank them all collectively, except for one group. These people can be identified because their contribution is so manifest and without it the book would certainly not be what it is – they are those whose recipes, words of wisdom and bright ideas comprise the text of the book. The National Childbirth Trust acknowledges their help with gratitude: Jane and Ron Daguerre, Evelyn Davidson, Wendy Evans, Sally Foster, Alison Gaffney, Judy Green, Kathleen Hallam, Harry Lewis, Deirdre Mackay, Marie-France Mackie, Tessa Mason, Frankie Morley, Liz Morrison, Ann Nutman, Brigid Oates, Jean Pengelly, Alison Phelps, Janet Smith, Jeanette Stevens, Beverly Holbrook Treen, Alex White, Jill Wiseman.

Comments from many readers have helped make this revised edition a much better book. The encouragement we received from readers was a great tonic too, making us know it was worth going forward with the project. In particular we should thank: Margaret Brady, Heda Borton (Pioneer Health Centre), Brenda Crowe, Celia Firmin (District Dietitian, Dewsbury), Rosemary Fost (NCT), Mavis Gunther, Peter Mansfield, Roy Meadow (Professor of Paediatrics, St James's University Hospital, Leeds), Elizabeth Morse (British Nutrition Foundation), Diane Souter (Senior Dietitian, Children's Hospital, Sheffield), The McCarrison Society, Margaret Wynn.

Foreword

This is a cookbook with a lot of refreshing differences. Instead of being full of recipes for the dinner parties you seldom give, the leftovers you feed to the cat or the soya mince you feel you ought to serve but never do, it is full of people. There are babies having their first tastes of anything other than milk and older babies who cannot wait until lunch-time. There are fussy toddlers and sweet-toothed schoolchildren. There are hungry, busy adults, visiting families and birthday guests. . . . It is a book about families and food, for families buying, cooking and eating food.

For me, the book's small size and lack of presumption is one of its great virtues because food, that basic necessity, has become big business with a complexity to match. On the one hand we have supermarket shelves laden with 'foods' which are so convenient as to be unrecognisable either by eye or from the listed ingredients. On the other hand we have endless scare stories about all those additives and preservatives and these lay us open to yet another set of claims; those of the health food business. What should we buy? What should our families eat? What is this stuff anyway? The greengrocer's wares are still familiar but are they not covered with pesticides or grown in lead-laden soil? Meat and dairy produce are good for us – or are they? 'Protein . . .' mutters one harassed shopper. 'Animal fats . . .' answers another. For our babies we go to quite another shop or set of shelves for special 'babyfoods'. No wonder many families avoid the whole issue when it comes to feeding babies, sticking exclusively to those tiny cans and jars as if 'babyfood' were somehow different, better and safer than 'real food'.

This book gives clear and forthright nutritional guidance and recipes to match. While not everyone will agree with every word of its nutritional standpoint, I believe that it cuts the problems of feeding a family down to size and that almost everyone will learn something from it as well as finding dishes which are fun to make and fun to eat.

If your family eats out of packets and cans, caring little what is in them and relying on plenty of added sugar and many stock cubes for meal-time pleasure, you may find yourself reminded that eating and being nourished are not always the same thing. But if yours is a family where nobody has time to play because it takes so long to soften the soya beans, you may find yourself agreeing that a packet pudding for supper is a small price to pay for an afternoon in the park.

Weaning a baby? There is no magic in special 'babyfoods'. Babies are human and, like the rest of us, they just need good food. Adapting what the rest of you are eating to a new digestion and a lack of teeth is as quick as it is sensible.

Feeding a milk-hating toddler? Despite those advertising hoardings there is nothing in milk which she cannot get from other foods. You can even make that same milk into yogurt or cream cheese which she might actually enjoy.

Holding back on cakes with a child who loves sweet things? Cakes need not be 'empty calories'. There are cakes here which are excellent food and will be irresistible to all of you.

Bored of cooking? There are new foods to cook, new ways to cook them and suggestions about letting the children cook too. Why not? The kitchen is for everybody just as the food which comes out of it via this book is for the whole family.

Penelope Leach

Contents

Weights and measures used in this book

The cup measure used is 1 (US) cup=240 ml/8 fl. oz or ½ (US) pint.
The tablespoons and teaspoons are level (unless specified otherwise),
  3 teaspoons=1 tablespoon.
The weight measures are US or imperial (1lb=16oz) and metric
  (1 kilo=1000 grams).
The conversions have been calculated to a convenient equivalent for the
  recipe in question, sometimes rounding up, sometimes rounding down.

Conversion tables

Weight measurements
  (exact)
  1oz= 28·35g
  2oz= 56·7g
  4oz=113·4g
  8oz=226·8g
  12oz=340·2g
  16oz=453·6g=1lb

Approximate conversion
  25g=1oz
  100g=3½oz
  125g=4½oz
  250g=9oz
  500g=1lb 1½oz
  1000g=2lb 3oz=1 kilogram

Liquid or volume measures
1 (US) fl. oz=28ml
1 (Imp) fl. oz=28ml

1 (US) cup=½ pint=8 fl. oz=240ml
1 (Imp) cup=½ pint=10 fl. oz=280ml

1 litre=1000 g/ml=1¾ (Imp) pints=35 fl. oz

Oven temperatures

	Gas	Fahrenheit	Centigrade
Cool	¼–½	250°	121°
Very slow	1	275°	135°
Slow	2–3	300–325°	149–163°
Moderate	4–5	350–375°	177–190°
Moderately hot	6	400°	205°
Hot	7	425°	218°
Very hot	8–9	450–475°	232–246°

Handy measures

Because we have standardised all the volume measures to US cups,
tablespoons and teaspoons, we give here the equivalent weights for
certain basic ingredients for those unfamiliar with the American system.
Conversely, those unused to weighing things can read the chart in the
other direction. If you lack a kitchen measuring jug, containers from

cream, yogurt, cottage cheese, etc., showing their capacity, can sometimes be substituted.

US CUP=8 fl. oz

1 cup sugar (most kinds)=225g/8oz
1 cup honey=325g/11½oz
1 cup butter or oil=225g/8 oz
1 cup white flour=125g/4oz
1 cup fine wholewheat
 flour=125g/4oz
1 cup coarse wholewheat
 flour=105g/3¾oz

1 cup polenta (maize
 meal)=125g/4oz
1 cup coconut=100g/3½oz
1 cup muesli base=100g/3½oz
1 cup rolled oats=85g/3oz
1 cup sesame seeds=140g/5oz
1 cup sunflower seeds=155g/5½oz
1 cup dry beans=190g/6¾oz

For more detail see the *Joy of Cooking* (see Book List). It has a 10-page central section on measuring.

Introduction

NOW WE ARE PARENTS, HOW DO WE COOK?

This book is directed to the problems people face as new parents in adapting their eating and cooking habits to suit family life.

It is written by members of the Leeds Branch of The National Childbirth Trust, based on their experience, such as it is. It is not an authority on the subject, but rather a resource book with ideas that may or may not appeal or apply to you and which you can follow up in the way that best suits your circumstances.

All the recipes should work both in the culinary sense and in the gastronomic sense. But, since we all know that however much one child may like a dish another may not, we give no promises beyond the knowledge that somebody's child has enjoyed each recipe.

We have tried to pay attention to the nutritional value of each recipe, at the same time realising that in everyday life the interests of nutrition are often in conflict with what children actually like and what is easy to make, not to mention what you happen to have in the house. It is better to whip up an instant pudding or open a tin, having spent the afternoon playing with the children (which is what family life is all about really), than to serve a lot of ill-tempered people a delightful concoction that is good for them. Better still, serve instant wholefoods – omelette, salad, cheese, fruit.

Cooking is an area where creativity is possible even for the most housebound parent. You can invent your own dishes, discover what your family most enjoys, work out weekly menus fulfilling its nutritional needs. The trouble is that if you're overtired and distracted from a stream of sustained thought, as most mums usually are, cooking is likely to become a real chore. We hope you'll find some of your work done for you here.

FEEDING A FAMILY – WHY IT'S WORTH TRYING TO GET IT RIGHT

'When I was a child,' a friend commented recently, 'I was told to eat a little of everything because it was all good for me. I still eat a bit of everything, but because it's probably all bad for me.'

It's easy to feel confused and unsure about what to give one's family to eat these days with scares in the press about one foodstuff after another – often things *we* were brought up to think were good for us. How can we know what to do?

The attitude above represents the best general advice: spread the risk by eating a little of a great variety of foods (and because they are good too). There is enough agreement on some issues, however, to give more precise guidelines:

1 Whatever you eat do not overeat and do not teach your children to overeat.
2 Cut down on sugar in all its forms including honey, but most particularly in its most refined forms.
3 Reduce the proportion of animal (saturated) to vegetable (poly-unsaturated) fats. Their proportion in your diet should be under thirty per cent of the calories taken.
4 Eat wholefoods, fresh foods and raw foods where possible. Grow your own food.
5 Use junk foods (empty calorie convenience foods) with discretion.

Katharine Whitehorn has written in *The Observer* on 'Good bad food'. Why *do* we like soggy chips, she asked. Answer, good bad food is food we had as children. She went on to discuss the dilemma a mother faces on learning that her child's favourite food is a newly discovered poison. 'When I wonder what to feed them,' she said, 'I fall back on the hash my mother served me.' And *this* is why it's worth trying to get that hash right. It is the food your children are going to feel is good for them whatever anyone says about it in their later lives. If the food and eating habits they grow up with really are good for them, you have given them a great asset.

DON'T SAY NOBODY TOLD YOU

An expectant mother is told she'll need a washing machine. She thinks it's for the nappies. Nobody tells her that her own clothes will need washing at least as frequently as the baby's. Suddenly her whole wardrobe needs radical reappraisal.

Somebody might tell you that household jobs will take roughly twice as long with a child in the house. Nobody tells you that on many days you'll get nothing done at all, nor that the first skill a new mother must learn is to do as many jobs as possible with a baby on one arm.

Before your baby arrives you may notice that houses where children live look different from yours, and you redesign your house, putting breakable and poisonous things on a higher level. But who tells you that a mobile baby is a household randomiser? Things don't stay where you put them any more.

Remaining flexible and adaptable to such changing demands is itself very demanding. If life with baby seems chaotic, don't despair. It won't go on for ever. Try to laugh because laughter is a wonderful remedy for tension. Relax consciously and then think how to use this period of flux positively. Let it be an opportunity to experiment with new ways of living.

On those aspects of living that concern cooking and eating we aim to inform you as to the best methods of preparing and serving food *other things being equal*. But let us be sure to tell you that in family life other things are rarely equal. You must make the best practical compromise to please the greatest number in your household, including yourself. Good food well prepared can contribute to the health and happiness of a family, but if you let its preparation or consumption become a source of unhappiness you are undermining its goal. Happiness is more important than food.

EATING THROUGH ONE'S DAY

It is arguably better for everyone's health to eat small but frequent meals than to wait until the end of the day for a big feast. It suits young children as well not to have to wait more than three or four hours between meals or snacks. From the point of view of their teeth, however, it is important for there to be periods as long as three or four hours where nothing is taken.

If you're free to organise your day as you please, then loosen up your thinking about when to eat during your day, and what kind of thing to have. Even if you agree that four or five small meals is a good idea, it is still good to have a balance of nutrients each time, so tea or coffee and biscuits is not as good as, say, fruit juice (giving some vitamin C) and homemade bread and cottage cheese. Also, try to have some meals where nothing sweet is taken, as much for the training of the palate as for the teeth.

Whatever you come up with when you work out what suits you and your baby's schedule, you will probably find that many factors interfere with a regular pattern, especially at first when babies seem to change their habits as soon as they've formed them. A routine is useful for weight-watching mothers and hungry toddlers because you know a meal is coming up soon and if you eat something substantial and satisfying (though not necessarily more than 300–500 calories' worth) you will feel less hungry during the gaps anyway. Your routine will have to take account of any fixed point in the day; school or work schedules, for example. You may also find a conflict between providing enough 'group time' at family meals and also having 'pair time' with different individuals in the family through the day. A compromise that might appeal is to eat something light with the children at 5 or 6; then, after the kids are in bed, the parents can have another part of their meal and chat together in peace.

SLIMMING

No longer is slimming desirable just to look good or feel good. It has been shown that you are more likely to die from being overweight than from most other general health hazards. New mothers face special problems in keeping their weight down, especially if they gained more than they meant to during pregnancy. They are likely to be spending more time per day near food than they were before, and when they start weaning their baby on to a mixed diet there will be lots of leftovers which will be better wasted than on their waistline (Mother's ruin).

The *Which? Way to Slim* is one sensible source of information on this subject. It exposes the many misleading ideas that prevail, such as that some foods are fattening and others slimming. The only known way to lose weight is to eat fewer calories than one uses up in energy. Of course some foods have more calories than others. Get a calorie counter to find out which ones. Let's look up potatoes: boiled new potatoes, 21 calories per oz; chips (thick cut), 39 calories per oz; chips (crinkle cut), 87 calories per oz; crisps, 159 calories per oz. The nutritional value has not increased with the calories! In general, note how easy it is to consume excess calories when eating sweet, fatty or low-fibre foods.

Keep fit exercises and becoming more active generally improve one's sense of well-being and probably help the right shape to emerge from a slimming regime. But don't pretend they use up all your excess calories. The unwelcome message is *eat less*.

Since Michel Guérard coined the phrase *Cuisine Minceur* (the title of his book of slimming cooking), many similar books have appeared in its wake which will be useful to serious slimmers and all those concerned to eat a low fat diet as well. Such people will find some suitable recipes in this book too (see Index under *low fat diet*). The crucial factor in weight control is to develop *and maintain* healthy eating habits.

DEVELOPING GOOD EATING HABITS IN YOUR CHILD

Attitudes to food run very deep in us. To help you decide how to set about helping your child to adopt healthy eating habits, start with these exercises:

1 Examine the meaning of food in personal relationships of importance to you.
2 Reflect on the meaning you have given food in your relationship with your partner and with each child.
3 Isolate from this study any rules and imperatives concerning food and meals (for example, 'You must have a square meal once a day', 'the Sunday roast must be on the table at 1 p.m. sharp', and other dos and don'ts about particular foods).

4 Consider the attitudes you'd like your children to have towards food and what you can do to foster these.
5 How can you develop the child's own jùdgement as to which foods are good for her, when she's had enough to eat, how often she should eat?
6 How are you going to set about finding out what will constitute a balanced diet for your child/family, given their likes and dislikes and the ease with which you can provide various foods?

These topics are very difficult to deal with; although there are no easy answers, it is worth thinking about them. The information one may find in health magazines is hard to deal with too; nutrition is a very complex business. Guard against thinking that because there is a food with something good in it the more you eat of it the better. Find out instead how much we need on average, and check that there is not some other thing in it that is harmful. Sheila Bingham's *Nutrition* is useful, or the HMSO *Manual of Nutrition*.

CONSERVING FOOD VALUE

Many factors affect the nutrients in food, from growing it in good conditions to your body utilising it well. Cooking is one of the most easily controlled factors – up to 80 per cent of vitamin C can be lost and up to 90 per cent of the vitamin B group and minerals. Lysine, an important amino-acid, is partially destroyed by high temperatures, in boiled milk, roasted peanuts, etc.

COOKING

Where possible prepare the food at the last moment – especially salads. Never soak vegetables, just brush them carefully under the tap and pat dry. Conservative cooking preserves most value – that is, use little water and cook as quickly as possible. Best methods are pressure cooking (only if done carefully), steaming, or dicing and tossing in oil. Chinese stir frying is also excellent – use a heavy skillet or a wok, which can be obtained from specialist kitchen equipment shops. And if you do boil something, try to utilise the nutrient-rich water as well.

OILS AND FATS

The heat treatment that most oils and fats receive turns the valuable unsaturated fatty acids into saturated ones which help cholesterol build up (this also happens in deep frying, roasted nuts, etc.). Rancidity, caused by long exposure to the air, destroys vitamins A, E and K, so store in closed containers in a cool place or fridge.

Light also destroys vitamins (milk can lose 70 per cent of its ribo-flavin in 2 hours), as do medicines, tobacco, nitrate fertilisers, sugar, bicarbonate of soda and, most important, stress.

Natural Balanced Eating has a vital principle whereby different elements work together to encourage the best possible utilisation by the body. Thus vitamin A is only properly assimilated in the presence of fats and oils; vitamin C and iron work together; so do vitamin D and calcium; incomplete proteins complement each other; and so on.

WHAT YOU CAN DO

Avoid the above harmful practices where you can (though it's no good becoming neurotic about it). Introducing some highly concentrated sources of nourishment such as wheatgerm or soya flour, sunflower or sesame seeds, molasses or skim milk powder and the like, can help you cut down on quantity while improving quality. For example, see uses of the Cornell triple rich flour formula (pp. 23 and 81). Eat as many fresh and vital foods as possible – raw if you can. Even in winter one can grow mustard and cress, bean sprouts and herbs on the window sill, and fermented milks like yogurt and kefir are fun to make. However, as important as the food we eat and the losses it incurs is our own mental and physical state. Nerves and tension can seriously impair utilisation as can disease and other physical imbalance. So don't worry about your food but be sensible and enjoy your time in the kitchen and at the table.

SECTION I
FEEDING BABIES IN THEIR FIRST YEAR

Good Food for Pregnancy and Breastfeeding

Any time is a good time to develop healthy eating habits and the best way is to start at the beginning when you want to have a baby or know one is on the way. Often you want to eat different things when you are pregnant and this is a good time to learn what really tastes good to you.

In general, eat a balanced diet from a wide variety of foods, a little of everything and nothing in excess. It is good to eat four or five small meals to keep your energy up and a continual flow of nutrients going to the baby. It will help you avoid excessive weight gain and prevent heartburn.

You can feel confident that you and your baby are being well nourished if you are eating predominantly: fresh fruit and vegetables (raw as much as possible), beans, pulses, grains and seeds including bread (preferably homemade with as much wholemeal flour as you like). Fresh meat, eggs and dairy products are all good in moderate amounts. Have fish occasionally (fresh and small are better than large and tinned) and liver or kidney if you wish (though some people think their likely lead content should rule them out).

A high carbohydrate diet may suit a sufferer of pregnancy sickness and it should be perfectly possible to ensure adequate nutrition through it.

Everyone would do well to avoid as far as possible foods containing additives, especially dyes in the yellow-orange-pink-red-brown range, and sodium nitrite (a preservative used in processed cheese and pink meats like bacon, corned beef, sausage).

If you are putting on fat (as well as weight) look for 'empty calories' (sugar, sweet things and junk foods) to cut out. Fats are not required above a daily minimum of 50g/2oz, which need not come out of the butter dish but will be better found, together with vitamins A and D, in foods such as fatty fish, cheese and eggs. Only linoleic acid (found in various vegetable oils and chicken fat notably) is a necessary nutrient the body cannot manufacture. Other essential fatty acids can be synthesised in the body.

Remember that the more wholesome the general basis of your diet, the more readily your system can tolerate the occasional less healthy thing.

Alcohol itself is a junk food (albeit sometimes accompanied by nutrients, such as the iron and calcium in red wine). Furthermore, there is evidence that it can damage the foetus in some cases. Undoubtedly the safest course for pregnant women and those hoping to conceive is to cut out alcoholic drinks. The problem is that it's before your pregnancy is confirmed during days 1–30 that the most fundamental damage would occur should you be one of the few unlucky ones. In fact, we all have a greater or lesser tendency to produce abnormal babies. In order to give our genes the best chance of producing a healthy baby we should eliminate as many predisposing factors as we can. Alcohol is such a factor. Smoking is another. If you can't cut them out, it is still good to cut down. Also, steer clear of every pill and potion except those knowingly prescribed by your doctor. See Roy Meadow, 'Drugs, diet and disease in pregnancy', NAMCW Conference Report 1978; *Alcohol and the Unborn Child*, National Council of Women Report 1980.

BREASTFEEDING

We believe that breastfeeding is the best way to feed a baby and the longer the better (but every day is worth it). The colostrum of the first days is especially valuable. The best way to get good advice on the subject is to write to the NCT Headquarters in London, or contact an NCT breastfeeding counsellor in your area (see also 'Breastfeeding' in the Book List). For this reason our advice on weaning assumes you are breastfeeding. Mothers who are bottle-feeding are generally advised to begin mixed feeding sooner (around 4½–5 months) and to wean to cow's milk at about 8 months. If the milk is pasteurised and kept in the fridge it can be used straight from the bottle.

Eating well while breastfeeding may not seem easy, as you need to take as much rest as you can between feeds. If preparing 'proper meals' seems beyond you, good ideas for quick nourishment can be found in Sheila Kitzinger's *The Experience of Breastfeeding* (Pelican), Chapter 14. Otherwise, continue to eat, as you have done during pregnancy and when you were preparing for pregnancy, the same well-balanced diet with nothing in excess.

You may find yourself wanting extra fluids. Drink water or fruit juice for preference, there is no need to increase your consumption of milk. In general, don't worry about foods you eat upsetting the baby, but if you become convinced there is an association with some particular food, mention it to your doctor. Follow your appetite and remember that breastfeeding does use up extra calories. Provide these ideally from wholegrain products such as wholewheat bread or pasta, brown rice and muesli, potatoes, beans or pulses, rather than from increased 'protein foods'. It's not a good idea to try to lose weight at this time. Your postnatal exercises can help you regain your figure and any extra weight you still have after the birth of your baby will eventually go.

Homemade soups, which you can reheat at any time, make a good quick snack with wholewheat bread. Salads or simply raw vegetables (sticks of celery, carrots, whatever appeals to you) provide valuable nutrients, need no preparation and are satisfying to chew. Use the time you save relaxing or playing with the baby.

Teeth

IN PREGNANCY Make sure there is plenty of calcium in your diet. There are many sources of this beside milk, of which oily fish including bones (like sprats) are particularly good as they also contain vitamin D and phosphorus, which helps the calcium do its job.

It is now believed that your taking of fluoride can't help your baby's teeth *in utero* although they are forming in the gums, as it doesn't pass through the placenta.

BABIES Permanent teeth are forming as soon as baby is born and before the milk teeth appear. There is good evidence that fluoride strengthens the enamel against decay. Discuss it with your dentist after you have read the evidence and check whether there is fluoride in your water supply already. Those wishing to hear the case against fluoride can contact the Anti-Fluoridation Campaign, or read the Templegarth leaflet on 'Fluoride, Teeth and General Health'. (See useful addresses, also Sheila Bingham's book in the Book List.)

Sweet teething lotions or jellies are harmful to teeth and gums. It is preferable to give your baby something cool to chew on like a spoon. Sometimes you can soothe sore gums by rubbing them, but often the child will not let you touch his mouth. He will like being cuddled and distracted from his discomfort. Give as much attention as you can at these times. Avoid sweet vitamin C drinks. There is no extra need for this vitamin for breastfed babies. Bottle-fed babies can be given vitamin drops, or, when mixed feeding begins, fresh fruit, vegetables, or their juices (see p. 26). Water (boiled for babies under 10 months), a healthy and cheap drink, is a good ally for your child's teeth. Come back with it every so often if the baby rejects his first taste.

TODDLERS From an early age your child should be helped to form the habit of brushing teeth after food is taken. Don't fight over it though; he'll like it better as a game even if he doesn't do it well and in due course he will be keen to learn to brush his teeth properly. A child who might swallow toothpaste or mouth washings should not be given toothpaste containing fluoride. A wholefood diet including plenty of chewing promotes the health of teeth and gums. The jaw bones then develop well to prevent overcrowding of the teeth later.

Weaning to a Mixed Diet

Opinions differ and so surely do babies about when is the best time to start the introduction of foods other than milk. If everything is going well do not think about it until your baby is 6 months old. Everything does not always go well, however; the baby may seem hungry and, if your sources of good advice agree, you could begin to give him something else at about 4–5 months. Do not pin any hopes on getting him to sleep through the night this way; it doesn't seem to work.

One danger of beginning before 3 months is that of encouraging a tendency to obesity in the baby. If you do start early with solid food, watch baby's weight and cut out cereals if he's getting fat. Another risk is that of provoking allergic reactions in the child because his digestive system is immature.*

If there is a history of allergies, hay fever, eczema or asthma in your families it would be wise to consult an authoritative source before introducing food other than breastmilk since your baby stands a greater chance than others of being among the 10 per cent with a disposition to allergy. The foods most commonly provoking reactions are milk, cheese, egg (especially the white), wheat, fish (especially shellfish), bananas, tomatoes, strawberries, meat (especially pork and beef), nuts and chocolate. Even if you expect no trouble, proceed cautiously with these foods. Observe your baby after his first tastes, making sure he has tried only one new thing within each 4-day period. Once he has taken to it, Kenda and Williams (see Book List) recommend you to use that food at least once every week. Food additives and highly processed foods may also provoke allergic reactions.

You will find that appetite along with growth and development generally comes in spurts. Sometimes the child will appear to survive on thin air, at other times he will get through enormous meals. Learn to trust his sense of what he needs. The development of a sensitivity to your child as an individual and responsiveness to his needs will be more valuable to you both than advice from others.

Note: We have been alerted to reports of botulism in infants being associated with the taking of honey in several cases in the USA over the past few years. No proven case in the UK is known to the Public Health Laboratories to date. Nevertheless, the interests of caution would be served by refraining from giving honey to children under 6 months (another reason to delay mixed feeding).

FIRST TASTES

Each baby's family's food is specific to him. He was nourished on it in the womb and thus his body knows it. Tastes pass into the breastmilk and become familiar that way. An eminently reasonable initiation to 'solid' food is to serve the baby from the family menu. Even better, let him show his readiness by taking food from your plate. The more you build on the familiar at each stage, the easier it will be.

1   Take your time over the introduction of foods other than milk. Start with tastes once a day and gradually over a few weeks build up to giving him, if he wants it, a small helping of fruit or vegetable purée. If he doesn't like it, stop and have another go in a few days' time. There is no hurry; the slower the changeover the better his system will be able to cope with the new foods. You can continue breastfeeding or bottle-feeding as before, allowing the baby to take less as time goes on.

2   To ease the job of his kidneys give plenty of water. It will not matter if you give too much: he can excrete it. What he cannot do is concentrate his urine. Therefore do not add salt or other flavours to his food.

3   Do not add sugar either. Babies do seem to show preference for sweeter tastes, so you may need to take the lead in educating him to enjoy natural sweetness. Even before the teeth appear they can be harmed by sugar on the gums. Indulging a taste for sweetness is likely to disadvantage your child with a tendency to obesity.

4   Keep his diet as low-fat as possible – he's getting enough fat from milk.

5   If you find yourself becoming too emotionally involved in feeding a baby, try to distance yourself a little. Laugh at yourself if you, quite understandably, feel rejected when he spits out your lovingly prepared food. Remember not to teach him to eat to please you, but to satisfy his needs. Never force a child to eat something. There is no food he must have. Find another food which fills the same dietary role as the rejected one.

Cooking and Serving Babyfoods

If you choose to use prepared instant foods, whether in tins, jars or packets, be sure to read the labels and find out about any additives you have not heard of. Where possible choose straight foods like apple, carrot or rice – or other fruits, vegetables or cereals – rather than 'dinners' or 'puddings'. Prefer the foods with fewest additives. Ingredients are listed in order, greatest quantities first.

COOKING YOUR OWN BABYFOODS

Properly organised, the task of cooking your baby's food is not as troublesome as you may think, and the food will almost certainly be better for him.

1 Meat, poultry, fish, vegetables and fruit may all be prepared in the normal way, except for a reduction in or elimination of salt, spices, herbs and other seasonings, and preferably cooked in a low-fat way. The meals in the 'Family Meals' section are designed for families including babies. Baby's portion should be removed before the seasonings are added, and chopped finely, sieved or blended. See also the instructions under the various 'Basic Staples' which follow (pp. 16–24).
2 Observe high standards of cleanliness in preparing babyfoods, especially at first. Wash fruit and vegetables carefully (to remove insecticides and preservatives that may have been used). Use clean utensils, don't taste the food with the stirring spoon, etc. Throw away any food left on the plate (bacteria multiply very rapidly in half-eaten food). Waste can be reduced by serving small portions at a time. Sterilise equipment if baby has a tummy upset.
3 Equipment needed: a strong stainless steel sieve is all you really need – better still, two; a finer one for liquids, a coarser mesh for puréeing foods. For information on other methods of making babyfoods, consult books in the Book List. Small heatproof dishes are useful for reheating refrigerated or frozen food.

If you want to prepare in advance your homemade convenience foods, you will need a fridge or a freezer with the capacity to quick-freeze. You can put dollops of food on tinfoil to freeze or use ice-cube trays. Turn out frozen cubes or dollops into plastic freezer bags and store in freezer. Economy of your effort is achieved and variety provided for the baby if you make a habit of cooking a little extra every time and freezing the surplus. When you go visiting you can take a frozen cube for baby's meal.

Re-served food should be brought to a complete boil, especially for a young baby.

A blender or mouli-légumes (not a 'Baby Mouli', which is a waste of time) is useful to prepare big quantities of purée.

For the equipment needed to make yogurt, see pp. 21–2.

SERVING BABY'S FOOD

1   Serve hot meals a little cooler than blood heat. Test on the back of your hand.

2   Endeavour to make meal times relaxed occasions. If the baby is frantic for a milk feed give it to him first, especially in the period between first tastes and the establishment of a mixed diet. Try to be ready ahead so *you* are not panicking either. Hold the baby on your lap for his first tastes of new food, so that everything isn't strange at once.

3   A simple plastic baby dish with raised sides (for when he starts to feed himself) can be used to serve his food in (there is no need for elaborate dishes which keep the food warm; the baby is unlikely to care). A rather flat plastic spoon available at baby shops is best for weaning.

4   At any time from 6–7 months onwards your baby will enjoy feeding himself. Never leave a baby unattended with finger foods, in case he chokes. To be extra safe, give only food that can dissolve, such as toast. If you cannot remove food from the mouth of a choking baby, hold him upside down and thump him between the shoulder-blades.

Guidelines for Vegetarians

1 The advice given here on weaning and on basic staples can be followed equally well by mothers wishing to wean their babies on to a vegetarian diet, except for the meat sources of iron and protein. Vegan mothers (who use no animal products at all) should seek special advice (see addresses, p. 118) for the making of grain milks, the many uses of soya products and the balancing of the diet for growing children, and ways to avoid a deficiency in vitamin B_{12}.

2 Iron: women (especially pregnant and nursing mothers) and children (especially in adolescence) are the people who need iron the most for growth and replacement of blood cells.

Shellfish, sardines (and such fish) and soya beans are the best non-meat sources of iron, for although many vegetables are rich in iron they often contain other substances which interfere with the absorption of it. The presence of vitamin C can lessen this effect, so take it with dark green vegetables, wholegrain cereals and pulses, nuts, cocoa and eggs. Some food such as dried fruits and molasses or anything you cut or cook with iron utensils have achieved their iron content from such utensils. It is uncertain whether iron in this form can be utilised.

3 Nuts and seeds for babies under one year (or perhaps much older) should be ground. Use a pestle and mortar for small quantities, or a coffee grinder for larger amounts.

4 Beans and pulses should be cooked whole but sieved for a small baby. A blender which cuts the skins very small can be used as an intermediate stage before simply cutting the beans in half for children of 2 years or more.

5 A baby (vegetarian or not) with cow's milk allergy can be given one of the several brands of plant and nut 'milks' suitable for bottle-fed babies. Check that it *is* suitable. Goat's milk (boiled and diluted) should be used only as a 'top up' for babies under 4 months.

Basic Staples for Babies
given in the most desirable order of introduction

Once you have established that your baby likes and can eat the following foods (see 'Weaning to a mixed diet', pp. 11–12), you can introduce other flavours with them for the sake of both variety and experiment. Each adapts itself well to blending flavours. New tastes can be introduced through the familiar ones and gradually you can isolate the new food to be savoured on its own.

1   *FRUITS AND VEGETABLES (for vitamin C in particular)*

BANANA (could be baby's first fruit unless apple is preferred)
Mash, blend or sieve fresh, ripe banana (the riper the better). If you want to be really careful, slit banana lengthwise and remove the line of seeds the first time you give it, but you will no doubt find that your baby can tolerate these tiny seeds without difficulty. Mash with a fork for a young baby. Serve with
(a) other fruits or juices,
(b) a milk-based product like yogurt or cottage cheese,
(c) baby cereal with milk or juice or water (avoid wheat at first; later, ground rice, Weetabix and breadcrumbs are acceptable),
(d) egg, for example raw egg yolk (though it is more digestible lightly cooked), egg custard.
Freeze whole or in long slices and offer as finger food.
   Poach in a light syrup made with a cup of water and ¼ cup sultanas or raisins soaked and then brought to the boil with a vanilla pod for flavour. Simmer 10 minutes and remove pod. Strain the juice for a baby. An older child can have the sultanas. (*Flamber* with rum for the parents!)

APPLE (a good bland fruit which is unlikely to cause allergy)
(a) Fresh. Even a tiny baby can take apple fresh but, since it loses vitamins once grated (as much as in cooking), prepare it as he is eating or just before. Grate finely, cover with orange juice (to prevent it going brown – also a delicious combination good for adult slimmers), serve at once. Other variations: grate into yogurt, cereal mixed with milk or juice, mashed banana or boiled custard.
      Another technique is to peel apple and hold in one hand, then run a spoon across it to scrape off a small amount and straight into baby's mouth. Start again.
(b) Cooked (or tinned). Slice apple, cook with a little water, cover pan but keep a watch on it. As soon as it is mushy enough to push through a sieve, turn off heat and taste. Add as little sugar as needed

to soften a very sharp taste; it may well need none. Stir in and allow to dissolve in hot juice. Push through a tamis or sieve, fine enough to catch peel, pips and pip cases. If you prefer to use an electric blender you will need to peel and core the apple first. When the baby is older only core the apple – the peel will grind up small enough in the blender, but if there are any bits left remove before serving to the baby. Serve warm or cold, with yogurt or custard. Warm, it could be mixed with breadcrumbs (put a little cinnamon and sugar on top for an older child).

You can bake apples whole (cored) and scoop out the soft pulp for baby. When cold, blend purée with stiffly beaten egg white (when baby can take it) for an apple snow, sweetened if necessary.

Other fruits to use in similar ways are pears, peaches, plums, apricots. Wash well and soak dried ones first before stewing. Do the same for prunes, but remember to keep an eye on the other end of the digestive tract and don't give them again if they seem to cause unusually loose stools.

AVOCADO

The avocado stands between fruit and vegetables as it blends so well with many different flavours. It is a good source of many nutrients and vitamins. Ripen the avocado at home. Use when it yields to gentle pressure.

Here are some suggestions for its use as a weaning food and during the first year:

Sieve and dilute with milk or yogurt to serve as a soup.
Mash with baked potato (without its jacket) or other vegetables.
Mash (or, later, dice) with fruit or juices.
Dice and serve with salad vegetables (see p. 67).
Spread on small fingers of bread or toast.

COOL GUACAMOLE

Half a mashed avocado
1 chopped, seeded and skinned
  tomato
1 tablespoon yogurt

A little finely chopped de-stringed celery. Blend all ingredients together and serve with bread or rice.

TOFU (soya bean curd)

See recipe for homemade tofu on p. 37, and also pp. 58–9.
A valuable source of many nutrients including calcium, iron and protein, and very bland to the taste, tofu is a useful weaning food, adaptable to many other tastes. Make little marble-sized balls of the homemade kind and roll in sprouted alfalfa seeds, gomasio (p. 54) or coconut.

VEGETABLES

CARROT (usually enjoyed as soon as tasted and a rich source of vitamin A)

(a) Raw. Grate very finely on a nutmeg grater; serve at once (see p. 67).
(b) Cooked. Carrots may be steamed, baked in the oven in a covered casserole dish lightly oiled, or sliced and cooked in milk or stock (keep the liquid for baby to drink or to use with cereal). If you are cooking a stew, put an extra carrot in for the baby and purée with some of the cooking liquid. Do the same with soups and stock. Mash hot carrot with a raw egg yolk (which will cook adequately in the purée) or use a sieved hard-boiled egg yolk.

Mix carrot with potato or other vegetables to introduce them as new flavours, then try them separately and show the plate with the different coloured dobs of purée so he doesn't learn that all food is mushy brown.

Make up baby cereal with cooking water or stock and add puréed carrot.

POTATO (another easy food that is seldom disliked and more nutritious than often given credit for)

It is best not to peel the potato before cooking, but you must cut out any bad bits and wash (preferably brush) the skin clean. Cook as soon as prepared: keeping them in water wastes water-soluble vitamins and some minerals. Do not overcook and serve immediately when done (this applies to all vegetables). Avoid boiling potatoes except in soups. In preference, steam them or cook in stews and casseroles, or bake them in their jackets.

Mash with yogurt or egg, gravy/stew liquid or stock (avoiding wheat-flour thickening until the baby has been introduced to wheat). Mash with milk or yogurt to mix with greens.

2   FOODS FOR PROTEIN AND IRON

Babies need less protein than you may imagine. It is pointless to give more than they need as the body simply converts to energy or fat what is left after the essential body needs have been satisfied.

Proteins are contained in many foods; in general animal sources are better assimilated than vegetable sources, but if care is taken to complement the various incomplete proteins in the right way (see p. 53) they will be as good as any source. See also tofu (p. 17). The presence of vitamin C makes iron in food more available. Meat, too, helps the absorption of iron from vegetables (see also p. 15).

EGG is a versatile and well loved food. Take care to observe how the baby responds to it. Delay giving the egg white until 8–9 months and only offer it if the yolk has already been accepted. (See p. 81.)

Eggs provide protein in a way that can be readily assimilated and, although not much iron, it is in the most readily available form. The protein is better digested when the egg has been cooked, but take care not to overcook to the point of toughness. Begin with the yolk only (for egg whites, see Index). Take it from a lightly boiled or poached egg, or mix it with something hot (like potato, apple, mixed cereal). Removed from fire, it will cook adequately in the dish. A hard-boiled yolk can be sieved, mixed with yogurt or freshly grated carrot, or spread on toast. Eggs are also used in old-fashioned macaroni cheese (p. 112) – serve as a purée.

Egg custard (p. 20) is a favourite and blends well with many other foods.

MEATS are generally good sources of iron as well as protein.

Fish and poultry have little iron but are good low-fat sources of protein.

Liver and kidney are rich in iron and many other nutrients; they are easy to sieve and serve with many of these basic staples. Raw lean meat may be scraped with a sharp or serrated knife; wipe off each scraping on to a plate and cook over a saucepan of water covered with another plate. It can also be stewed and puréed for babies. Skim cooled fat off roasting juices and serve the jelly to the baby on toast, in soup, or mashed with vegetables.

BAKED EGG CUSTARD

3–4 eggs
25g/1oz sugar (try muscovado)
½l/1 pint milk
nutmeg

Whisk eggs and sugar lightly. Warm milk but do not boil. Pour milk over the eggs and strain into a buttered ovenproof dish. Stand in a tin of water. Top with nutmeg. Cook until set at 300° (gas mark 1–2) – about an hour. A knife should come out clean.

Variations
1 *Bread and butter pudding* Add chopped sultanas or sticky raisins (remove pips) to custard and place buttered bread on top. Cook as above.
2 *Good daughter pudding* (for adults, if you wish, having made a small plain custard for the baby). Spread bread with mincemeat and place in layers in the dish. Cover with custard and cook at 325–350° (Gas mark 3–4) for between 30 minutes and 1 hour.

BOILED EGG CUSTARD

2 egg yolks
2 tablespoons sugar
240 ml/½ pint milk (heated)
   vanilla (use a pod to flavour
   the milk if you have one)

Cream yolks with sugar until white and fluffy. Add heated milk gradually. Cook the custard in a double boiler or in a heatproof jug in a pan of water over the heat. Stir constantly around the sides and across the bottom. It is cooked when it coats the back of a wooden spoon. This takes about 20 minutes. Cool quickly.

Variation
Banana custard Pour cooled custard over sliced or mashed banana (depending on the age of the baby). Grate a little nutmeg on top. Purée in a blender if the baby dislikes lumps.

3 CALCIUM FOODS

YOGURT (from about 6 months; arguably safer than boiled milk as a first taste of cow's milk as the lactose which some indicate as a cause of allergy is converted to lactic acid; however, some babies are still allergic to yogurt)

(a) Serve blended with vegetable or fruit purées (freshly grated or sieved, mashed or cooked purées).
(b) Yogurt is good used like cream or salad cream on jellies, cake or salads (see p. 67). It can be served with custard or other puddings and can make readymade foods less sweet.
(c) Cook with it, using yogurt instead of milk in white sauce (after the baby has accepted wheat), in scrambled eggs, pancakes, cakes and biscuits or baked fish.
(d) Yogurt ices for babies over 6 months can be made by blending equal quantities of yogurt and fruit purée, with a little honey or sugar to sweeten and whipped egg white (if accepted by the baby). See Sylvia Hull in the Book List.

COTTAGE CHEESE (same indications as yogurt; lactose is changed in cheese too)

Not all babies like the consistency of cottage cheese, but because of this it provides a new experience for the baby and so is worth trying. It has the same dietary role as yogurt and can serve similar culinary uses too. You can try sieving it if the baby hates lumps. It can be thinned with milk.

Many other foods contain calcium. If your baby can't (or won't) take cow's milk don't worry and don't force her. Try DRIED FIGS (sieve pips out carefully), FISH (especially boney fish like sardines), SOYA FLOUR, and SESAME SEEDS (ground or tahini). GREEN VEGE-TABLES (especially watercress and parsley) are quite rich in calcium but also contain oxalic acid, which hinders its absorption.

MAKING YOGURT

Yogurt is a good weaning food as the lactose is converted to lactic acid, which makes it easier to digest, even for many adults. If you want it thicker in consistency, either reduce the milk or add powdered skim milk at the rate of up to 25g per 600ml/1oz per pint. Make sure a small baby is drinking water if you reduce the water content of the yogurt this way. You will find that yogurt is not difficult to make yourself. Rather than investing in an expensive yogurt maker, buy instead a good cooking thermometer, with the range 100–212°F included, to help you carry out the following instructions:

1 First scald the milk (already thickened with milk powder if desired) to kill off any bugs; heat the milk to 180°F; it will taste better for not boiling.
2 Pour scalded milk into container(s) – see below – this will have the effect of scalding them as well.
3 Let it cool to 110–120°F (rather above blood heat, hot to the hand).
4 Mix your starter (any plain yogurt, commercial or homemade, should work) at the rate of ½ teaspoon per 600 ml/pint of milk, with a little of the heated milk in a cup, to thin it down so it will blend evenly through the rest of the milk.
5 Now add starter mixture evenly to the milk in the container(s). Stir briefly and gently.
6 Your milk will turn to yogurt in about 4–8 hours if kept warm. If it has not set when you look at it, put it back for another hour or longer. As soon as it is right, remove and refrigerate. Keep a little aside as your next starter.

Equipment If you have no place in the house that is reliably constantly warm, use a thermos flask, and decant the yogurt, once made, into jars or plastic containers. A homemade yogurt nest we know consists of a plastic bucket, lined with 2cm/1in thick foam (inside polythene bags to keep clean), including a piece on the bottom and top. It houses three jars which fit neatly and keep each other warm on the haybox principle. Look about your house for something that suits your conditions and available materials, remembering that the essential thing is simply to hold the milk at just *above* blood heat (106–115°F) for 4–8 hours. That is all an electric yogurt maker does. A simple kit which the non-DIY-minded may prefer is available from large baby stores.

Alternative method   An even easier recipe for those who like the taste of UHT milk, and which will work well provided you keep the equipment meticulously clean, involves making yogurt in a casserole dish (preferably pyrex) kept warm over a pilot light, on a storage heater or in a plate-warming oven. You need heat the milk only to 110°F (hot to the hand) and you may even have success without heating first. Otherwise follow points 4–6 above.

In fact, any kind of milk can be used – UHT, evaporated or powdered milk or a combination of any of these.

SOUR CREAM. Use fresh single cream and follow steps 1–6, or UHT cream and proceed as for the alternative method above. Cultured sour cream could also be used as a starter.

SOFT WHITE CHEESE can be made from yogurt. Simply line a colander with muslin (a former nappy is ideal) and empty on to it about twice as much yogurt as you require cheese. Gather up the edges of the muslin and tie around a wooden spoon placed across a bucket or deep basin. Leave in a cool place for 1–8 hours, depending on how stiff a cheese you want. Refrigerate in a covered container. Use the whey in cakes or bread.

4   *CEREALS* (for protein, B vitamins and fibre)

Although they were once a favoured first food, it is now considered wise to postpone the introduction of cereals until after fruits and vegetables have been accepted, which means waiting until about 8 months, if you have started other foods at 6 months.

Because of the danger of provoking an allergic reaction it is also strongly recommended to delay giving wheat (with its high gluten content) until your baby is 8 or 9 months and is better able to digest the cereal protein.

Rice is a good cereal to begin with. Where possible avoid highly processed instant varieties and sweetened cereals. Ground rice which needs cooking is not as simple to prepare, but likely to be better for the baby.

It is *so* useful to be able to thicken sloppy food with instant cereal to get exactly the right texture that you may find you want to use it. Make the best judgement you can, taking everything into account. When the baby is able to take wheat, bits of bread can take over this role.

Hundred-per-cent cereals are best, where the whole grain is used. These include wheat flakes, shredded wheat, porridge, and muesli (see recipes on pp. 24 and 69). Wheat flakes compressed into biscuits are a great favourite with many children. It is easy to introduce variety through this staple. Serve dry with butter and Marmite (but not too often for young babies), with peanut butter or with soft white cheese. Moisten with stock as a savoury dish or serve with vegetable purées. And, of course, in the usual way with milk, hot or cold, with fruit purées or yogurt.

HOMEMADE BREAD

When your baby is able to take wheat, and when he is able to manage finger food, it is a good time to consider making your own bread. You will know exactly what has gone into it. You can enrich it with milk, egg, soya flour, molasses, or by using the Cornell triple rich flour formula (for each cup of flour called for, add first 1 tablespoon soya flour, 1 tablespoon powdered skim milk, and 1 teaspoon wheatgerm; fill up with the flour of your choice, preferably wholemeal). Then it is a balanced food in itself with a good protein content, so you don't need to worry so much what the baby has with it. If he's off savoury foods, no matter. Let him have something sweet on it; the bread is so good in itself. Experiment to find a kind of bread that he likes and which is also good for him. Bread is useful in so many ways, apart from the obvious – slices, sandwiches, and toast (try toasting just one side, then put sardines, banana or Marmite on the other side and frizzle under the grill). Think also of its use in little squares in liquid food – soups, gravy, stews, etc. – for mopping up. This makes it easier for little ones to manage these foods. There is also the old favourite, bread and milk. Then there are breadcrumbs, which can be added to soft boiled eggs, mixed with fish cooked in milk, or the like. It is also good mixed with puréed fruit or as topping (see Sylvia Hull's puddings in *Cooking for a Baby*).

See also pp. 31–5; 'spreads' (pp. 36–8); and 'finger foods' (pp. 25 and 68).

HOMEMADE RUSKS

You can make rusks for your baby by simply slicing old bread into sticks about an inch square and drying them off in a very slow oven, or in the oven drawer, or putting them in a hot oven you have turned off. You can also make *Melba Toast*, or *Fairy Bread*, as some call it, by slicing stale bread very thin and drying off in the same way on oven trays.

TEETHING BISCUITS

³/₄ cup baby rice cereal	Mix with water until stiff. Roll out
¹/₄ cup cornflour	and cut into hand-size pieces.
2 tablespoons sugar	Bake at 350°F (gas mark 4) for 15
2 tablespoons cooking oil	minutes. From 5 months.
1¹/₂ tablespoons baby milk powder	

GRAHAM CRACKERS

$^1/_2$ cup margarine
$^1/_2$ cup brown sugar
$2^3/_4$ cups wholewheat flour
($^1/_2$ teaspoon salt)
$^1/_2$ teaspoon baking-powder
$^1/_8$ teaspoon cinnamon

Cream margarine and sugar. Mix dry ingredients and add to the creamed mixture alternately with $^1/_2$ cup water. Mix well. Let stand 30 minutes. Roll out dough on a floured board to 3mm/$^1/_8$ inch thick. Cut into 5cm/2 inch squares and bake on an oiled baking tray at 350°/gas mark 4 for 20 minutes.

BABY MUESLI

For babies from 6 months to 1 year   Soak a heaped teaspoon of finest oatmeal or other fine flakes in warm water. Add a teaspoon of sweetened condensed milk (or baby milk powder or yogurt and a little honey), a little nut cream and a few drops of lemon juice with grated apple or sieved berries.

For babies over 1 year   Soak 1 tablespoon of fine flakes in water. Add a tablespoon of sweetened condensed milk or yogurt and honey, then an apple grated, skin and all, and grated or ground nuts sprinkled over the top.

Snacks and Drinks

FINGER FOOD SNACKS

(Patience preservers – give when baby can't wait for his meal)

Try a few of the following on a plate for children of any age starting around 12 months:

1 Pieces of raw vegetables, carrot sticks, cauliflower trees, green or red peppers, bean sprouts, baby beetroot, raw mushrooms, etc.
2 Cut up pieces of fresh or dried fruits – apricots, apples, peaches, dates, raisins or sultanas.
3 An ice cube, perhaps made from fruit juice or yogurt; frozen seedless grapes, banana, peas, strawberries.
4 Pieces of cheese. Keep trying different kinds: the child can learn to extend his repertoire. Never scold him for refusing new foods, but offer them in a free 'take it or leave it' atmosphere. You may find it worth offering a second time something first rejected.
5 Tiny snack crackers, melba toast or bread with peanut butter, Marmite or Barmene, cheese spread, pâté (see pp. 36–8 and 68).
6 Remove string from well scrubbed celery sticks and fill with soft white cheese, peanut butter, sesame or sunflower spreads (such seeds can be ground and mixed with peanut butter).
7 Dry breakfast cereals – a few cornflakes, rice crispies, puffed wheat and so on in preference to sugared kinds or potato crisps.
8 Any new food you'd like your baby to try (see 4, above). Hunger sauce often helps.

EGG NOG

Any member of the family over 6 months will appreciate this. A good pick-me-up after naps or when everyone has just come in tired after a day out.

1 egg (or egg yolk)
1 cup milk
1 teaspoon carob powder or cocoa
  a dash of vanilla, or
1 teaspoon malt drink powder
1 teaspoon honey
1 ice cube (optional)
1 banana (optional) or other fruit

Blend until frothy, in an electric blender. Or, without the optional ingredients, beat with a whisk or hand beater. Experiment with different flavours, using available fresh fruits – berries are all good. Use immediately to avoid losing vitamins from the fruit. It is rich for a baby, so make sure he has plenty of water that day.

OTHER DRINKS FOR BABIES AND CHILDREN

Water is an excellent drink, especially good for babies as they should take everything more diluted than older children or adults. You can dilute fruit juices by half. *Broths* can also be diluted and served with meals. If you have a juicer, *fresh fruit and vegetable juices* are unbeatable for taste and value. Tomato juice, freshly made and sieved, is more acceptable than orange to some babies. Otherwise a blender will make a variety of natural fruit milk shakes, nut-milks and lovely blended fruit drinks. Also try soaking dried fruit overnight in plentiful water – a sweet juice is the result. Apricots, apples and raisins all make very popular juices. Instead of the stimulating chocolate or cocoa drinks, try blending a little carob flour with milk or water – it is both nutritious and pleasant. Many herbs and spices are loved as flavourings to children's drinks – anise or fennel seed, ginger, cinnamon, mints, lemon balm, lavender, meadowsweet . . . the possibilities are endless. A medicinal herb drink can be used as the base and flavoured with anise, mint and blackberry or elderberry syrup.

SECTION II
FAMILY MEALS

Eating together as a Family

THE OCCASION   Make family meals happy, relaxed, pleasant, sharing times. The emphasis should be on developing the forgotten art of conversation rather than an occasion for recriminatory remarks about behaviour.

ORGANISATION   The key to realising this desirable state of affairs is good planning, admittedly a difficult thing to achieve considering the incidents which interfere with even the best regulated households. 'Keeping one's cool' is a great aid to coping, and being one step ahead is a good way of promoting both.

SUITABLE STYLES OF COOKING   There are two main alternatives. The first is prepared food which can be made when it best suits you during the day and reheated later, for example casseroles reheated while potatoes in their jackets cook. You can spend time with the children, easing them through a likely crotchety time of day (easing stress in the family system is a valuable function). The other kind is the meal in a minute, for example pancakes or stir-fried vegetables.

The first kind of cooking works on blending flavours (as in soups) and softening textures through cooking (lentil purée, spaghetti sauce); the second kind uses interesting juxtapositions of texture or flavour (fresh figs and soft cheese, Asperges Fontenelle – asparagus dipped in a soft-boiled egg). Sophisticated cooking doesn't mean putting wine and spices into everything. Look for the subtler harmonies of whole foods.

SPICE IT AT THE TABLE   When a baby is sharing your food it is best to add no salt, pepper or other spice. Get yourself a pepper grinder (black pepper is better) and a salt grinder, and use freely on your food at the table. A more elaborate selection of sauces, pickles and other condiments such as Parmesan cheese may also be presented for adults to use as they like (see p. 54).

Holidays at Home

Catering for a family, possibly with extra guests, over a period when shops are shut requires careful planning.

1 **INTERWEAVING INGREDIENTS** Get several versatile basic foods in quantity, such as big joints of meat, poultry, or beans and grains which will provide a variety of different appearances on the table – hot, cold, in soups, risottos or whatever. A supply of other less usual ingredients will add a special note to these dishes. Again versatility is a virtue, so pick things like bean and seed sprouts, mushrooms, green and red peppers. Olives, anchovies, shrimps and stem ginger can be bought in jars or tins and kept for unscheduled use. Your basic supplies will probably be taking up all available fridge space, so plan on using a few good keepers like rice, and other cereals or pulses (see also p. 30).

2 **EATING ALTERNATIVE STYLE** Try a different style of food for a few days. Vegetarian meals are good because most ingredients last well. Get right into a new cookbook, using it exclusively for some days. Go ethnic and try eating any national cuisine that requires particular ingredients which you need to buy in quantities larger than for one meal. According to Michel Guérard, the founder of the new wave of slimming cooking, his *cuisine minceur* should be followed for a week at a time. Non-slimmers at your table can be provided with cheese and biscuits, dried fruits and nuts at the end of the meal.

The trick is to get things prepared in advance so that each meal can be quickly thrown together, allowing you time with your guests. A freezer is a boon, but attention given to a sequence of dishes, each using up perishable leftovers and drawing progressively on ingredients which are growing or preserved or which keep well, can provide as workable a scheme as any freezer. Use the expertise you build up to make every week's work easier.

On Holiday without a Fridge

Grains and pulses are useful as they store well. Not so easy to cook on camping gaz, however, so make the compromise you prefer between the extra weight of precooked grains and the nuisance of cooking for an hour or more. A pressure cooker cuts cooking time. Take hard-boiled eggs, they will travel better. Use in salads, sandwiches, and in sauces with tuna, shrimps or vegetables such as courgettes. Use tinned fish (scares notwithstanding). Bean sprouts are again a boon, and.can be carried between layers of damp cloth in transit.

Nuts, seeds and dried fruits travel well, and are compact and light-weight for their energy value. Take care that young children eating them sit still and chew well. It is wise to avoid giving them peanuts altogether.

Cheese (especially the maturing kind like Camembert) keeps better than milk so take your dairy produce in this form, using evaporated milk to put in coffee, and yogurt with breakfast cereal. Porridge can be made with water and served with butter and sugar (or evaporated milk). Alternatively, have muesli cookies or toast for breakfast.

Fresh fruit and vegetables are not a real problem either without a fridge. Especially if they are growing! Use a cellar if available, or keep outside if you can. No perishables should be kept in a heated room in winter.

IDEAS FOR SPECIAL MEALS IN THESE CONDITIONS

Smorgasbord Serve a herring or fish/seafood dish, meatballs (see recipe) or sliced sausage or ham, and lastly a platter of Scandinavian cheese with crispbreads or fresh rye bread. Tomato, cucumber, beetroot, pickled cucumbers, fresh dill-weed, parsley and chives are all suitable garnishes/side dishes.

Chinese dishes, cooked in a wok, especially where there's just one gas ring.

Baking Your Own Bread

WHY BOTHER? Homemade bread tastes better. You can easily produce a wide variety of flavours and textures, and of shapes and sizes (tin loaves, cobs, rolls . . .); you can ensure the nutritive value of your bread, and reduce or eliminate additives. You can make bread attractive for the children, and adapt it to special dietary needs. British factory bread is surely the worst in Europe – more tasteless, and more chemically dosed, than any other.

IS IT TIME-CONSUMING? For most of the time between starting work on a batch of bread and taking it out of the oven, you leave the process to carry on by itself. It can be over within 1½ hours of starting (if you give it a boost with vitamin C), typically takes 3–5 hours, but can be extended over two or more days (with the help of refrigerator or freezer). In any case, the amount of your own time involved in the making of one batch of loaves or rolls will usually be under twenty minutes (if you do the mixing and kneading yourself) or about ten minutes (if you delegate these tasks to an electric mixer).

Perhaps you think of kneading as hard work. Certainly it uses more calories than beating an egg, but you do not require any special strength for the job. It's as easy as leaning on a table, once you realise that you can make your weight, not your arms, do the work.

HOW DO YOU MAKE BREAD? Mix flour, water, a little salt, and yeast (proportions roughly, to 450g/1lb flour: 250ml/½pt (10 fl. oz) water, 1 teaspoon salt, 15g/½oz yeast – less yeast in proportion for bigger batches). Knead the resulting dough. Leave to rise (prove). Knead lightly again, shape into loaves or rolls, place in tins or on trays, leave again to rise. Bake.

Many variations are possible on this basic theme. Water may be partly or wholly replaced by milk, or other liquids (for example eggs or oil) may be added with compensating reduction in the basic liquid; with similar compensation, dry ingredients such as ground cereals, soya flour or mashed potato may be added to the recipe. Fresh yeast may be replaced by dried yeast granules, at the rate (for bread) of ⅓ the weight of fresh yeast, and appropriately reconstituted before use. The dough may be given one rising only, in the tin – this is usual for bread made entirely with wholemeal flour – but in general the more risings, and the slower each rise, the better the bread. Slow rising results from reducing the proportion of yeast, using cooler ingredients, or a cooler place for the rising. A 'pre-rising' may be given with a sponge batter mixed from all the yeast liquid but only part of the flour (and no salt yet – salt inhibits the action of the yeast); the complete dough may be allowed to rise twice in the bowl before the single rise in the tin.

For a good rise, and so a lighter bread, you need a 'strong' flour (brown wheatmeal or white, labelled 'strong' or 'bread flour') and thorough kneading. A dough made entirely from wholewheat flour rises less and does not have to be kneaded. To enjoy the flavour of wheat you must use flour with the germ left in (in practice this means using at least part wholemeal, which contains all the bran too, providing roughage and also a good proportion of protein, vitamins and minerals). Milk in the liquid, dried milk dissolved in it, an egg included in it, or soya flour replacing 60g/2oz of each 500g/lb of strong flour will each add interest and variety to flavour and increase the protein content of your slice of bread.

Very easy ways of starting breadmaking are buying prepared bread mixes (already containing dried yeast) or soda bread mixes (for example Scofa meal) or buying a dough hook for your electric mixer, if you have one – and following the instructions.

But making bread without such artificial aids is still easy.

BROWN BREAD (OR ROLLS)

750g/1½lb flour (all wheatmeal or 1lb strong white, ½lb wholemeal)
450ml/15oz warm water (for rolls, 50–50 milk and water)
1–2 teaspoons salt
15g/½oz fresh yeast (or 1 level teaspoon dried yeast granules, reconstituted with a little of the water and a pinch of sugar)

Yield: 1 large loaf *or* 2 small loaves *or* 16 small rolls.

If you are using dried yeast, first measure the water (or milk and water) and use a little of it to reconstitute the granules: allow it 20 minutes. Weigh out the flour, mix in the salt. To hasten matters, leave the flour in a very warm place until warm to the touch. Cream the yeast and a little liquid. Add the rest of the liquid to this (or, if using dried yeast, to the yeast liquid you have already prepared). Place the flour in mixing bowl, make a well in the middle, pour in the yeast liquid and mix thoroughly (the human hand is an unrivalled mixing implement – have a scraper ready to return mixture to the bowl from said implement, and a bowl of water to rinse it quickly if the doorbell rings). The dough will become stiff, but not too dry to mop up all the flour (after you loosen any residues with hand or spoon) and so clean the bowl. Flour a board, deposit your lump of dough on it, and knead it – folding it towards you like an omelette, pressing down on it, then giving it a quarter turn and repeating the action. Five minutes' kneading will probably suffice – enough is when the dough gets less sticky, and starts to push back at you when you press down. Grease or oil the bowl, replace the dough in it, empty it out again into your hand and then put it back into the bowl the other way up (so that the top is oiled too – to stop it drying out and cracking). Cover the bowl with a thick layer of folded damp towel or teacloth, or put the whole thing into a plastic bag (for example a clean rubbish bag) and leave to rise until doubled in bulk. Remove the covering, punch down the dough, turn out onto a floured board and shape for the oven. Place in greased tin(s) – rolls on baking trays, leaving space between for expansion – cover and allow to rise a second time (first rising takes up to 2 hours at room temperature, second about 45 minutes for bread, 20 minutes for rolls). Preheat oven to 450°/gas mark 8. Bake for 35 minutes (bread), 15–20 minutes (rolls). Check for doneness by tapping the bottom of the loaf or roll – if it sounds hollow, it's done; if dull and solid, give another 5 minutes and try again. Cool on racks away from draughts.

SHAPES Baking loaves in tins is easiest, and the dough 'rises' upwards rather than sideways. To get a tin loaf to rise evenly, it helps to shape the dough by flattening it into an oval with a rolling pin, rolling up the oval like a carpet, and then pinching the end seam. Finally roll the ends flat, tuck them under and pinch the seams just made. Then, when you place the dough in the tin, press it flat with your knuckles, pushing it out to the corners (this helps the rise). Many shapes are possible for loaves baked on sheets rather than in tins – plaits are fun (see our Sourdough recipe), a cob is the simplest, the cottage loaf very difficult. The dough for these free-standing loaves must not be slack (wet) or it will not hold its shape, and it is still good to 'wind it up' into the chosen shape, as in the flattening and rolling procedure given above. Also, the second proving (on the baking sheet) should be shorter than for a tin loaf. With all loaves, cuts in the top can be made after shaping (try using scissors) – they open as the bread rises. For a crisp crust, brush or spray on water just before you put the bread in the oven.

PIZZA

An easy meal to prepare when you are making bread anyway is pizza. Press down a ball of dough into a well oiled flan tin and top with thick tomato and onion sauce, anchovies or tuna, cheese, olives, mushrooms, green pepper, oregano or herbs to taste. Bake at 425°/gas mark 7 for 15 minutes and at 375°/gas mark 5 for a further 15 minutes.

SOURDOUGH BREAD

If you like experimenting with your breadmaking try baking sourdough bread. This is a very ancient kind of bread, as sourdough starters were used to make dough rise probably long before yeast from fermenting ale or wine. A starter was a treasured possession of the pioneers of the American West. Some people claim that this bread is more beneficial to health than yeast bread. It does not crumble when cut. (If you would like to read more about sourdough, see the books by Edward Espe Brown and Rita Davenport in the Book List.)

NB You must only use utensils of earthenware, glass, plastic and wood to prepare your bread so that the dough does not acquire a bitter taste from metal.

SOURDOUGH STARTER

2 cups plain flour
2 cups lukewarm water

1 tablespoon dry yeast*
3 tablespoons sugar or honey

Mix dry ingredients, then stir in water gradually with *wooden* spoon. Cover with clean towel and place in warm spot to sour. Inspect every day and stir to see if it has developed a sour aroma. It will take 2–5 days to develop a sour aroma, after which it is ready for use. Keep in the fridge and use at least once a week. If you don't want to use the starter as often as that, you will have to 'feed' it by adding small and equal quantities of flour and warm water. It can be frozen – just leave it in a warm place to reactivate when next you want to use it.

*Should you be out of yeast, the starter is likely to work without it by trapping wild yeast in the air.

SOURDOUGH BREAD

Night before baking
Mix together with *wooden* spoon
1 cup starter
3 cups flour (81% wheatmeal and/or wholewheat)
2½ cups lukewarm water

Morning
Take 1 cup of mixture and replenish starter pot in fridge

Add to remainder
70ml/2½ fl. oz oil
2 teaspoons salt
3–5 cups flour – enough to make a kneadable dough of your chosen mixture of whole rye flour, wholewheat and 81% wheatmeal

Mix all the ingredients in a bowl until too thick to mix, then knead thoroughly, bearing in mind that sourdough is a bit stickier than yeast dough. Return to bowl and leave to rise for at least 2 hours. Punch it down in the bowl and make tin loaves or plaits.

Tin Loaves   Divide the dough in two, form two loaves which will half fill your tins. Leaves to rise until level with tin (about 1 hour).

Plaits   Divide the dough in six, roll out into six strands. Make plaits of three strands each. Brush with milk and sprinkle with sesame seeds. Leave to rise for 15 minutes.

Baking   Bake at 425° (gas mark 7) for 20 minutes, then 375° (gas mark 5) for 30–35 minutes (loaves) and 15–20 minutes (plaits) or until done. The bottom of the loaves should sound hollow when tapped. You might have to turn them upside down and return to the oven for a few minutes.

Spreads

FOR STARTERS, SNACKS, OPEN-FACED SANDWICH BASES, PACKED LUNCHES

ALTERNATIVES TO BUTTER IN SANDWICHES

Use cottage cheese, soft white cheese or mayonnaise with salad fillings; peanut butter (with added milk powder or sunflower seeds to enhance the protein) or spreads in these pages; scrambled egg alone or with added herbs such as parsley and chives, paprika or curry powder, chopped peppers; chutneys or pickles; tofu.

SANDWICH SPREAD

2 hard-boiled eggs
3 tablespoons salad cream or yogurt
2 tomatoes
salt and pepper if liked

Mash the hard boiled eggs and chop the tomatoes. Put into a liquidiser with the rest of the ingredients and liquidise until smooth. You can add chopped cucumber, spring onions, beansprouts, as you fancy. Skin the tomatoes if you prefer them like that.

TOMATO AND CHEESE SPREAD

50g/2oz margarine/butter
50g/2oz cheese
250g/½lb ripe tomatoes
2 large tablespoons breadcrumbs
salt and pepper
lemon juice

Scald and skin the tomatoes, cut them up into small pieces, grate the cheese. Melt the butter in a pan. Add the cheese and tomatoes, and cook for 5 minutes. Remove from heat, add crumbs and seasoning, and turn out into cold pot.

HOMEMADE TOFU (soya bean curd)

For 450g/1lb tofu:
225g/8oz soya flour
850ml/1½ pints cold water
juice of two lemons
½ teaspoon sea salt

Empty flour on to water in a good sized heavy saucepan, bring to the boil and simmer gently for 5 minutes, then stir in the lemon juice and leave the mixture to cool and thicken. Line a large sieve or colander with a double layer of butter muslin (a new life for a muslin nappy!) and pour in cooled soya mixture. Gather up ends of muslin and tie together to make a bag and suspend from a wooden spoon across a bowl or bucket. Leave it to drip in a cool place for 8–12 hours. Keep in a covered container in the fridge. Use as a base for babyfoods (see p. 17), or instead of butter in sandwiches.

TOFU SPREAD

225g/8oz tofu
1–2 tablespoons tamari or soya
  sauce
1–2 spring onions finely chopped
1–2 tablespoons green pepper
  finely chopped
optional extras: a little pressed
garlic or grated fresh ginger, anise
seeds or coriander.

Mix ingredients together and store in an airtight container in the fridge. Serve on bread or toast, on savoury biscuits or in sandwiches. Fill celery sticks or wrap in lettuce leaves for a nutritious low-calorie snack.

HOUMUS

2/3 cups chick peas (garbanzos)
2–5 tablespoons tahini (sesame
  paste)
finely chopped or pressed garlic
salt to taste
lemon juice (up to half a lemon)

Soak chick peas overnight. Cover with water and bring to the boil, skim, simmer until soft (at least an hour). Blend or purée to a smooth paste, adding cooking water as necessary. Stir in rest of ingredients.

FRENCH CHICKEN LIVER PÂTÉ

300g/8oz chicken livers
equal quantity bacon bits
2 eggs
nutmeg
shallot and parsley
salt and pepper
(sherry or madeira to soak livers in
   overnight optional for adults)

Remove any stringy white pieces from livers and mince with bacon and shallot. Mix in eggs and chopped parsley. Season with nutmeg and pepper, using a few whole peppercorns if you like, and a little salt. Pour the mixture into greased earthenware dishes (preferably with lids for storage later in the fridge). Cook in a *bain-marie* (dishes standing in water) for 2 hours at 300° (gas mark 2). A knife should come out clean when done and it will register 180° on a meat thermometer. Any child on a mixed diet can be offered this pâté: mix with cereal for a baby, or offer as finger food on bread.

KIPPER PÂTÉ

225g/8oz kipper fillets
100g/4oz unsalted butter or
   margarine
juice of ½ lemon
2 tablespoons tomato purée or
   ketchup
black pepper

Pour boiling water over the kippers to thaw if frozen, or to help remove skins in any case. Leave to cool. Remove skins, mash and pound to a paste or put through a sieve (to remove small bones from baby's portion). Add butter or margarine, lemon juice, pepper and tomato purée and pound till smooth.

Serve with dry toast as a starter or in sandwiches for a picnic or packed lunch.

Soups
(See also p. 63)

HUNGARIAN BEAN MINESTRONE

250g/½lb beans soaked overnight
(red kidney, rose coco or brown
beans give a good colour)
Add at least 4 vegetables, diced
finely in proportions and
quantities to taste (about
450g/½lb in all)
carrot
onion
celery
mushroom
tomatoes
parsnip
swede
a little capsicum
cabbage
florets of cauliflower
green beans
peas
spring onion

Add enough water to soaked
beans to make 1½–2 litres/3–4
pints of soup. Bring to boil, skim
and cook slowly for 1 hour. Never
add salt at first or the beans will
harden.

Then add recently chopped
vegetables and pasta, if liked.
Cook ½ hour, or until tender.

For adults, serve with grated
parmesan cheese sprinkled on top
and pepper and salt.

For little babies, purée a
portion. For older babies, cut the
beans and add pieces of bread to
soak up the liquid; then they can
eat it with their fingers.

To cool a child's portion rapidly
add a spoonful of frozen peas.

If liked, add soup pasta for the
last 15 minutes of cooking, or
however long it takes to cook.

CHICKEN SOUPS

Basic chicken stock
a chicken and giblets
1–2 litres/3 pints water
an onion stuck with a clove
a carrot (and parsnip)
some celery tops
bouquet garni (parsley, thyme,
bay)
salt and pepper

Parboil a chicken before roasting
for 10–30 minutes, or cook it
entirely in the pot for about 1
hour, with the vegetables and
seasoning. After the chicken is
eaten, add the broken bones and
simmer an hour more. When cool,
strain and keep the stock in
fridge.

Chicken liver soup

Keep the liver aside to cook for the minimum time (about 5 minutes)
frozen peas
cooked rice
chopped parsley and chives

Reheat stock with pieces of carrot chopped up in it and the peas and rice. Chop the liver finely when cooked and place in serving dish with fresh herbs. Pour in the hot soup.

Chicken noodle soup

fine vermicelli or soup pasta
bits of chicken
chopped parsley

Reduce stock by boiling without lid until it tastes good. Add noodles; cook 5–10 minutes. Add other ingredients.

Cream of chicken soup

chopped chicken
1 tablespoon flour
1 tablespoon margarine
up to half the liquid in milk
mushrooms or watercress (optional)

Gently fry mushrooms or watercress in margarine if using either optional extra. Add chicken and flour and then stock, then milk (or top of the milk). Reheat to just on boiling point. Serve.

MARROW BONE SOUP (as a meal)

1 marrowbone
1 onion, stuck with a clove
1 carrot (or more; cook a few for baby and refrigerate or freeze – their water-soluble vitamins will be in the soup)
Add if you have any of the following:
celery tops
leek tops
bouquet garni (parsley, bay leaf and thyme or marjoram)
lettuce or spinach leaf
parsnip, turnip, swede (not too much)

Place all ingredients in a pot with a lid, cover with cold water and bring to the boil. Skim, several times if necessary (helps to keep the soup clear). Simmer for 2 hours.

Your marrowbone consommé is ready. Add salt to taste for adults, having removed baby's portion. Keep some in the fridge to mix with cereal for savoury meals, or warm slightly and serve in a baby cup at meal times. Be careful to remove the fat from the soup before serving. Plunge the ladle to the bottom and allow fat to resettle before withdrawing ladle.

Before you serve the soup, into which you can put freshly chopped chives and parsley, you can serve the marrow on toast. This is especially nice on rye or wholewheat bread toasted. For adult palates add freshly ground sea salt and black pepper.

If your butcher has cut the bone into three pieces for you, there should be no trouble getting the marrow out. It is helpful to have a long-handled teaspoon. Place the marrow in a warm heatproof dish, and keep it warm if it is not to be eaten that minute.

SPLIT PEA OR LENTIL SOUP

450g/1lb dried peas (green rather than yellow) or lentils – big brown ones are best
2 medium carrots
2 big stalks of celery (including leaves)
1 onion
also, if available
1 leek
1 parsnip or piece of swede
a lettuce leaf
bay leaf and parsley and thyme
ham bone, bacon rind, chicken or turkey carcass (leave out for vegetarian version)

Soak the pulses overnight in water or stock. Make up the liquid to 3 or 4 pints and cook slowly for 2 hours, with the ham bone, bacon rind or poultry carcass.

Then chop the vegetables, add them to stock, and cook a further half hour. Push through mouli or tamis, or liquidise (having removed bones).

Bind the soup with a good tablespoon of *beurre manié* – butter or margarine with an equal quantity of plain flour (brown or white) worked into it.

Serve with rye bread, pumpernickel, or *croûtons* (inch cubes of bread fried in bacon fat for preference). If giving the latter to children make quite sure they are not too hot; they retain heat very well. Adults may like a dash of cayenne or tabasco to give the soup some piquancy.

If using ham bone or bacon rind, do not add extra salt until you have checked the taste.

Two Finnish Main-course Soups

FISH SOUP

500g/1lb vegetables: potatoes,
 carrots, peas, onion
a whole fish (any size up to
 750g/1½lb)
dill weed, parsley and/or chives
1 litre (2 pints) water or fish stock
salt and pepper
2 tablespoons butter or margarine,
 or 1 cup of cream (optional)

Peel and dice the vegetables. Boil
in the stock (or water) and simmer
until tender (about ½ hour). Add
the fish cut into 4cm/1–2 inch
chunks, and simmer gently until
done. Correct the seasoning. Pour
onto fresh herbs and butter and
serve.

CABBAGE AND SAUSAGE SOUP

500g/1lb white cabbage
boiled potatoes to taste (250g/
 ½lb)
boiling ring or Frankfurter
 sausages cut into 3cm/1-inch
 chunks
stock or water, 1 litre or more
salt
peppercorns
allspice or dill seeds or a little cardamom (anti-flatulent)

Slice the cabbage finely, place in
heavy soup pot and cover well with
water. Cook with pepper and salt
and spices until slightly chewy.
Add chunks of sausage and the
previously cooked potatoes and
bring back to the boil. Simmer for
5–10 minutes, adding more water
if necessary.
A dollop of yogurt is good in it.
Sprinkle with parsley.

Low-fat Ways of Cooking Fish

1 **IN MILK** A good method where some is to be taken for a baby.
Put fillets of white fish in pan, cover (or nearly cover) with milk, and
flavour with black pepper, nutmeg, and bay leaf for adults. Bring to the
boil. The milk will boil up over the fish. Cover and simmer until done,
which does not take long. Part the flesh in the thickest place. If it is all
white, then it is done. Make a white sauce with the milk. Use some to mix
with baby's portion (the tail end of a fillet rarely has bones in it – choose
this for baby, but check carefully all the same).

FISH PIE

any boned fish – mackerel is good and cheap
onion, chopped
milk or stock
leftover potatoes, mashed

Put pieces of fish in a pie dish with onions and liquid.

Spread mashed potatoes over the top and spread a little butter on top. Bake in the oven, approximately 375° (gas mark 5), for about 1 hour.

Good for the whole family. Mash together for a young baby (having checked out his portion very carefully for bones).

2 **GRILLING** Brush with oil on both sides and grill without turning fish.

3 **IN FOIL** Any fish from the finest salmon to the cheapest herring may be cooked this way. It is especially suitable for whole fish. Make sure the fish is properly cleaned, then place it on a generous amount of foil in an oval dish (for preference). Depending on the type of fish, choose seasoning: fennel or dill seeds usually blend well; try parsley, chopped shallot and pieces of tomato with white fish. Dill weed, parsley and lemon slices go well with oily fish. Smear French mustard inside herrings, or simply restrict yourself to salt and freshly ground black pepper. If you have any fish stock (or have time to make some by boiling up the fish head and any oddments, plus some slices of carrot, onion, bouquet garni, and a little white wine if available), add ¼ cup, or a tablespoon of water. Put on a little margarine. Now bring the sides of the foil together, well above the fish, fold over a couple of times and press together. Fold over ends and press together too, so that a loose foil package is now lying in your dish. The steam will be able to circulate inside the foil to cook the fish. Place in the oven. If you want it to take a longer time set it at mark 3 (325°) and leave 45 minutes before checking, depending on the size of fish. You will find, however, that it is also possible to cook at mark 6 (400°); a small fish may be done in 20 minutes cooked this way. It is cooked when the flesh parts easily from the bone – put a fork in gently beside the backbone to see how it is doing.

Try to lift pieces off the bones for baby, but still check that they are bone-free. You can cook this way very successfully on an open fire, but use double layer of foil to guard against sticks piercing the package.

Meat and Liver

KEBABS – COOKING ON A SKEWER

Kebabs provide an opportunity to treat your children to something they'll like. You can also slip in something they might not expect to like, such as kidney. Meats separated by bay leaves are best for adults, but children will like some vegetables on too. Always start and finish with meat as it shrinks in the cooking and will hold the kebab together. Grill in the oven, under the grill or over an open fire or barbecue. Serve with bread or on a bed of boiled rice with tossed green salad, tomato or grilled pepper salad (see below).

Make up your own selection (you can actually leave your guests to do it at a barbecue) from the following. If you improvise remember to put things together that require the same cooking time (for example don't put raw onion with tomato if you want the onion to cook):

Pieces of lean lamb, beef (not pork unless previously cooked);
Pieces of bacon, kidney, sausage (best to boil sausages first),
   Bratwurst, etc.;
Pieces of pineapple, green pepper, mushroom (soak in oil first).

It is best to make up the skewers in advance and marinate in oil and herbs for an hour or longer before cooking.

Good party food.

BALKAN GRILLED PEPPER SALAD

Grill red and green (and yellow if available) peppers until the skin is black all over and starting to peel off. Remove from grill and place in a brown paper bag, twist the bag closed and leave for 5–10 minutes. Now it should be easy to remove all the skin. Work under running water if it is still difficult, but avoid this if possible as it must wash the taste away. Slice the flesh of the peppers and discard the pips. Dress with oil and vinegar dressing.

USING UP LEFTOVER MEAT FROM THE EVER-POPULAR ROAST DINNER

MEAT FRITTERS

Minced leftover lamb or beef
a little bacon (if liked)
1 small onion (minced)
some bread to clear out mincer
1–2 eggs
up to ½ cup flour (any kind)
milk to mix
seasoning to taste (include thyme)
1 teaspoon oil

Keep this minced mixture to one side (about 1 cupful) while you make the batter. Sift flour and salt into a bowl (include some SR flour or add baking powder). Make a well and break egg(s) into it and oil, mix until the egg absorbs all the flour, then add milk gradually until a firmish batter is made. Add mince.

Drop in tablespoons onto a greased pan. Turn after a few minutes with an egg slice. When cooked through and brown on both sides, keep warm on brown paper to drain off fat. Serve with tomato sauce. Children really love these fritters – a safe bet for visitors.

STUFFING FOR PEPPERS OR MARROW

Minced leftover meat or poultry
Cook an equal quantity of whole
    grains (rice, wheat, rye, barley)
    or use part white rice if preferred
1 egg or 3 tablespoons tomato purée
spring onions or shallots
season to taste with chopped mint/
    basil, garlic and grated nutmeg,
    black pepper
tomatoes (fresh or canned)
½–1 cup stock
grated cheese
marrow or peppers

Blanch green peppers in boiling water for 5 minutes, marrow for 10–20 minutes, both whole. Cut in half lengthwise, remove pips and fill with stuffing. Press it down compactly, round the tops and grate cheese over them. Place in oven dish with lid. Put tomatoes and liquid around the side, add a clove of garlic and a few peppercorns to flavour sauce (thicken with tomato purée if necessary).

A vegetarian version would substitute chopped nuts for the minced meat.

SCANDINAVIAN MEATBALLS

450g/1lb finely minced meat
(beef and pork or beef only)
1 egg
1¹/₂ teaspoon salt
dash of pepper
dash of allspice (optional)
100ml/¹/₃ cup unseasoned
breadcrumbs
200ml/²/₃ cup single cream or milk
1 medium-sized onion
butter or margarine

Peel and grate or mince onion and fry it lightly for a milder taste, use it raw if you prefer the stronger taste. Soak the fresh breadcrumbs in cream. Mix the meat, egg, seasoning and grated onion. Add breadcrumbs to meat mixture and stir well.

Roll meatballs in wet hands. Keep on moistened cutting board until ready to fry in a generous amount of margarine. Don't fill the skillet more than two-thirds full and shake frequently to preserve round shape. Lower the heat and let them cook through (about 5 minutes altogether for small meatballs the size of marbles; about 8 minutes for larger ones the size of pingpong balls). If you fry a lot of meatballs the skillet may need washing (and drying) between every two or three batches. They freeze well, and may be served cold or hot or with gravy (freeze separately).

Children love the tiny-sized ones. For a party serve them on cocktail sticks to dip in tomato sauce.

Make gravy from the drippings in the pan with an addition of stock, bouillon cubes, soy sauce or a little flour burnt to a darker colour and moistened with water.

COOKING LIVER

Liver contains so many good things it is worth including in the family menu occasionally, as well as in baby's diet. But you do not need to prepare it the same way every time. For a start there are pâtés (recipe p. 38) and mousses, and there are many ways of serving it hot.

Liver is unpleasant when dry and hard. To avoid this result, cook at a slow heat and do not cook too long – it should be pink in the middle, a stage which occurs between its raw colour and a final brown colour. You will have to develop your own judgement as to when this occurs by slicing your pieces to have a look. Liver may be soaked in milk for up to 6 hours before cooking to make the flavour less strong and to help keep it moist.

CHICKEN LIVERS

Chicken livers are the mildest, and a good beginning for the liver novice. Soak them in milk, remove any stringy white pieces, but otherwise leave them whole. In an old flour bag place a couple of tablespoons of flour (any kind, try wholemeal), pepper and salt, a little red paprika or any spice you like, then drop the livers in, one by one, shaking the bag each time to coat them. Hold the top of the bag firmly and give a really good bouncy shake. Now heat a little margarine in a thick pan and fry the livers gently. Their taste may be further disguised/enhanced by chopping bacon and onion finely and frying that in the pan first, with a clove of garlic squeezed through a garlic press. Sliced mushrooms may be added too. Keep sauce warm while livers cook.

BERLIN LIVER

450g/1lb liver
3 cooking apples
3 onions
180g/6oz butter or margarine
sour cream or yogurt

Slice the onions into rings and cook gently in butter until soft, but not brown. Remove and keep warm while liver in ½-inch (1cm) slices is cooked in the same pan.

In a separate pan with fresh butter cook apples, peeled, cored and sliced into rings, until soft. Add cream or yogurt at the end. Serve with a very soft purée of potatoes.

SWEET AND SOUR LIVER OR PORK

1 small green pepper
1 small onion
1 small carrot
2 teaspoons oil
300ml/½ pint water or stock
3 tablespoons vinegar (cider is good)
2 tablespoons clear honey
1 rounded tablespoon cornflour
1 tablespoon soy sauce or tamari

225g/8oz wholemeal spaghetti rings or Chinese egg noodles
450g/1lb lean belly pork (spare ribs)
or liver and, to coat and fry liver,
3 level tablespoons wholemeal flour
salt and pepper
1 egg
4 tablespoons natural bran
3 tablespoons oil

Pork version only   Bake pork spare ribs or belly pork on a rack in an oven tray at 400°/gas mark 6 for 30 minutes.

Sweet and sour sauce (both versions)   Slice the onion, pepper and carrot into ½cm/¼-inch thick sticks. Heat 2 tablespoons oil (sesame if you have it) in a heavy saucepan. Fry onion until golden, add carrot and green pepper, and cook gently for a few minutes. Then add vinegar, bring to the boil, add honey and water or stock, bring back to the boil, cover, and simmer 5 minutes until carrots are nearly tender. Blend the cornflour with 2 tablespoons water and the soy sauce. Gradually stir into the sauce over the heat until it boils and becomes clear. Remove from heat.

Cook spaghetti rings in boiling water for 10–15 minutes. Keep warm in serving dish. Noodles take only 4–5 minutes.

Liver version only   Mix flour, salt and pepper together on a plate, beat egg on another plate, and place bran on a third plate. Coat liver pieces in seasoned flour, beaten egg, and bran. Shake off excess bran and fry liver in 3 tablespoons oil for 8–10 minutes, turning once when coating is browned.

Drain the liver or pork on kitchen paper and place down centre of pasta on serving dish. Reheat the sauce and pour a little over the liver. Serve the remainder in a sauce boat.

Casseroles and Leave-it-to-cook Meals

Once you master the basic technique for making a casserole, you can make up your own from what is to hand.

BASIC CASSEROLE RECIPE

Fry chopped or sliced onions until transparent, add garlic and any spices used. Then brown meat (if used), cut into cubes or convenient pieces – chops, say, or chicken joints – and dust with seasoned flour if you wish. Other vegetables, which can be browned or not, include carrots, celery, mushrooms, and peppers.

As soon as you put on the lid, escaping moisture is caught and they will start to stew. Lower heat or place in oven. Extra liquid may not be necessary; check during cooking. However, if you are including beans, pulses or grains you will need extra liquid, even if they've been soaked. Add, levelling off so they are covered by the tomato juice, vegetable water, stock or wine, which you can make up with water to the right quantity. As a general rule use more water for tougher meat and slower cooking at lower heat (not more than 300°/gas mark 2).

Add herbs last. Salt should be added after cooking beans and pulses to prevent their becoming hard. It can be a good idea to cook the meat (and onions) first for an hour, then add some vegetables to cook another hour, and finally, before serving, some frozen peas or greens to cook in last 10–15 minutes. Potatoes in their jackets will take about 1 hour at 350°/gas mark 4 cut in half, or longer at lower temperatures and if kept whole. Another way is to parboil them for 10 minutes and bake for 20 minutes

LAYER DINNER

Layer 1 Sautéed onion or leek

Layer 2 Brown rice, barley or potato

Layer 3 Sliced carrot or root vegetables

Layer 4 Green pepper or celery

Layer 5 Minced meat or brown lentils

Layer 6 Mushrooms, aubergines or tomatoes

Tomato juice or stock to cover

In a separate pan fry layer 1 gently; cover base of deep casserole dish. Then add other layers. If using aubergines, slice and sprinkle with salt and leave to drain for ½– 1 hour; wash and dry and sauté in olive oil (for preference). Cook for 2½ hours at 325°/gas mark 3. Serve sprinkled with parsley.

BOSTON BAKED BEANS

500g/1lb haricot beans
125g/¼lb salt belly of pork (omit
  for vegetarians)
1 teaspoon salt
½ cup black treacle
1 teaspoon dry mustard
1 tablespoon brown sugar or
  blackstrap molasses
1 small onion (optional)

Soak the beans overnight. Boil in 4 cups water for about 2 hours. Drain and reserve water. Cover belly of pork with boiling water and let stand. Drain and gash every few inches. Put beans in bean pot, pushing pork down until all but rind is covered. Mix salt, molasses, mustard and sugar. Add ½ cup reserved water and bring to boil. Add onion (if used); remove before serving. Pour boiling mixture over beans and add more water, enough to cover beans. Cover pot. Bake about 8 hours at 300°/gas mark 1. Uncover last hour to brown pork rind. Traditionally served with brown bread – a sort of steamed raisin bread. Try a salad too.

NEW ENGLAND MEAT LOAF (and soya version)

1 medium onion, minced or
  chopped
½ cup breadcrumbs
1 teaspoon each of salt and pepper
sage, thyme and oregano to
  taste
½ cup stock
4 sprigs parsley, finely chopped
3 tablespoons Parmesan cheese
  (or sharp Cheddar)
1 beaten egg
500g/1lb minced beef or 8oz dry
  soya beans and ½ cup
  wholewheat flour. Add 3
  tablespoons tamari or soya
  sauce to the stock in soya
  version.
225g/8oz canned tomatoes
1 teaspoon oregano

Sauté onion in butter. In a large bowl mix the breadcrumbs with herbs, seasonings and stock. Add onion, meat, parsley, cheese and egg. Blend together well, then form into a loaf in a baking pan. Bake for 30 minutes at 375°/gas mark 5. Now pour the tomatoes over the loaf and sprinkle on 1 teaspoon oregano. Bake 20 minutes more. Serve with baked potatoes in their jackets.

Soya version
Follow instructions for cooking soya beans on p. 57. Pass through blender or mouli-légumes. Add ½ cup of wholewheat flour and soya sauce or tamari to stock. Use in place of meat in recipe.

SWEET CORN BAKE

275g/11oz can of sweet corn
2 medium parboiled potatoes,
    diced
300ml/½ pint milk
2 eggs (or substitute 2 tablespoons
    soy flour)
50g/2oz butter
100g/4oz grated cheese
seasoning
some grated cheese mixed with
    breadcrumbs for topping
optional: finely chopped bacon in
    topping

Mix corn with milk, season well
with salt and pepper and bring to
the boil. Beat eggs (or mix soya
flour with some of the warm milk)
and stir into milk and corn; blend
well. Add the butter, cheese and
diced potatoes and mix
thoroughly. Turn into casserole
dish, cover with topping. Cook in
the centre of the oven at 325°/gas
mark 3 for about 1 hour until
topping looks golden.

CAULIFLOWER CHEESE WITH BACON

1 large cauliflower broken into
    florets
100g/4oz lean bacon, chopped
1 large onion, chopped
2 tablespoons butter
2 tablespoons flour
300ml/½ pint milk (or cooking
    water)
3 tablespoons cream or yogurt
125g/5oz Cheddar cheese
grated parsley

Steam cauliflower for 5–10
minutes. Drain and put aside.
Gently fry bacon until golden, and
remove from pan. Sauté onion in
bacon fat and butter until soft.
Add flour and cook for one
minute, stirring all the time.
Continue to stir, gradually adding
milk or cooking water, and bring
to the boil. Remove from heat and
add cream or yogurt and most of
the grated cheese. Stir in bacon
and season with salt, black pepper
and parsley. Pour over cauliflower
in an ovenproof dish. Sprinkle
with remaining cheese. Bake in
the oven at 375°/gas mark 5 for
30–40 minutes until brown and
bubbling.

SPAGHETTI SAUCE WITH MEAT OR LENTILS

1 tablespoon olive oil
1 onion, grated or minced
garlic to taste
250g/½lb lean minced meat (for a
    vegetarian version substitute ¾
    cup red lentils)
grated or minced carrot
100g/4oz mushrooms
½ green pepper, finely chopped
50g/2oz tomato paste
liquid, about 600ml/1pint
    including, as available and
    desirable, tomato juice, stock,
    water, wine
salt and pepper
cinnamon and paprika
parsley and bay leaf
oregano or marjoram or thyme
1 teaspoon French mustard
    (optional)

In olive oil (for the flavour) fry the
onion gently until transparent.
Add garlic, then meat (if used),
mushrooms, carrot and pepper.
Simmer 5 minutes. Add tomato
paste and stir in, then the liquid
and lentils (if used). Bring back to
the boil and adjust quantity of
liquid – it will take a fair bit. Add
seasonings and herbs, close lid
tightly and simmer gently for at
least an hour.
Serve with spaghetti (try
wholemeal) and top with
Parmesan cheese. Children may
prefer grated Edam cheese.

LASAGNE

Try the *Lasagne verde* (the green comes from spinach). Slip them into
cooking water one at a time and stir a teaspoon of oil into the water to
help keep pasta pieces apart. Alternatively, use any pasta shapes as other
kinds are much easier to cook. When nearly done, remove from heat and
drain. In a flat dish make layers of spaghetti sauce, pasta, sliced cheese
(Mozzarella, Edam, Gruyère), and extra oregano if liked, and top with a
béchamel sauce made from a tablespoon of butter or margarine, flour
(try half wholemeal) till absorbed, and 600ml/l pint of milk (or part
stock). Sprinkle Parmesan, oregano and black pepper over the top, and
breadcrumbs around the edges. This dish retains the heat well, so take
care when serving children. By the same token, it's a good dish for a
buffet party.

Vegetarian Meals

More and more people are eating vegetarian meals for at least part of their weekly menu. Nursing mothers may consider it wise to eat 'low on the food chain' where feasible. We try to explain here, very briefly, how you can be as well nourished, particularly with respect to protein. Apart from using soya beans, a well-known source of high-grade protein, the key lies in protein complementarity. This subject is developed in Frances Moore Lappé's *Diet for a Small Planet* (see Book List). Its companion volume, E. B. Ewald's *Recipes for a Small Planet* (Ballantine Books), translates the detail of the idea into recipes.

COMPLEMENTING PROTEINS

'First-class' or 'complete' protein means that the eight essential amino-acids are present in a food in the correct proportion. This is not the case with most vegetable protein foods such as beans, grains and seeds. By eating at the same meal, however, foods whose amino-acid contents complement each other, complete protein results. The foods should be eaten in the correct proportion for the maximum protein value. The diagram gives a rough guide to these proportions shown as volume

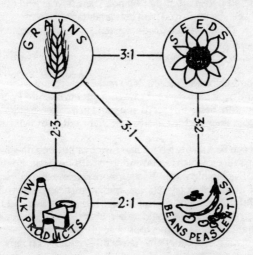

measures (in the case of milk products, milk is the basis of the calculation. Milk products with less water should be accordingly scaled down).

SOME COMPLETE VEGETABLE PROTEIN COMBINATIONS

GRAIN/BEAN Wholewheat soya bread, beans on toast, houmus on bread, bean curry with rice, bread with bean soup, bean or peanut and breadcrumb croquettes, grain and bean casserole (see *Pasta e Fagioli*).

GRAIN/SEEDS Bread, biscuits or cakes enriched with seed meal, bread and sesame or sunflower seed spread, rice with sesame or sunflower seeds or sprouts (see *Mixed grain salad*), grain dishes with *Gomasio* topping.

GRAIN/MILK PRODUCE Wholewheat bread with milk or cheese, pasta with cheese, cereals with milk, wheat or rice in cheese tart, soft white cheese on wholewheat cake (see *Orange Quark Torte*, *Rahkomenakakku*).

Condiments, Sauces and Dressings

Many grains and pulses are rather bland. Their flavour and often nutritional quality can be improved with condiments and sauces.

Barmene is a yeast extract product, similar to Marmite, containing vitamin B_{12}.

Tamari, miso, soya sauce are all fermented soya products with a pleasant strong taste.

Gomasio is popular with children. You make it by toasting sesame seeds on a tray in the oven until darker brown but not burnt. Add 1 part sea salt to 20 parts or more of sesame seeds and grind in a coffee grinder. Store in an airtight container and use instead of plain salt with bean and grain dishes.

Sauces Oil can be substituted for margarine or butter with wholewheat flour in white sauces, which can be enriched with soy flour. For liquid use milk, stock or vegetable water. Furthermore, miso, tamari or soya sauce can be used to enrich gravy; cheese, and yogurt, and egg yolk can be added to white sauce. For extra flavour, as appropriate, add sautéed mushrooms, onions, parsley and other herbs or spices, for example nutmeg, coriander seeds, fennel tops or seeds and paprika.

Seeds and nuts are especially nice toasted. Try toasted poppy seeds on pasta.

Chutneys and pickles can be made at home without additives (see p. 93).

YOGURT SALAD DRESSING

1 cup yogurt
juice of ½ lemon
¼ teaspoon of dry mustard
pepper and salt

optional additions
capers
paprika or tabasco
chives or other herbs
pressed garlic
mint (goes well with cucumber)
crushed coriander seeds
ginger (antiflatulent; include when
    using dressing on cabbage)

Mix the ingredients together in a jar or cocktail shaker and shake until blended.

This low-fat dressing is the ideal slimmers' slaw dressing. It is good on cucumber. Made hot (with chilli or tabasco), with coriander, garlic and mint, it makes a cucumber raita to accompany curries.

A good medium for bean sprout salad.

OIL AND VINEGAR DRESSING

In an old plastic container with a lid, sprinkle enough salt to cover your salad. Add 1 tablespoon of wine or cider vinegar and leave salt to dissolve. Then add freshly ground black pepper, a little mustard and herbs you fancy or pressed garlic and enough oil to make dressing up to ½ cup. Shake well with lid on. Pour onto salad when ready to serve to prevent green salad going limp.

SOYA MAYONNAISE

2 tablespoons soya flour
1 tablespoon honey
2 tablespoons lemon juice

Mix and add oil slowly until smooth. Good for cabbage slaws.

TAHINI DRESSING

tahini (sesame seed paste)
lemon juice
½ clove garlic, salt and pepper

Shake up in a jar until well blended. Good for grain salads.

Potatoes as a Base for Vegetarian Meals

Potatoes never need be peeled. They are best baked in their skins or steamed and mashed (skin and all – using a mouli-légumes to 'mash' retains some of the skin). Reconstitute dried milk with the cooking water (or other vegetable water) and mash in with the potatoes. In this way you can use potato for croquettes with cooked lentils or ground nuts and herbs. Look potatoes up in a food analysis chart if you need persuading that they are good. By all means add cheese, milk, eggs, etc., to jacket potatoes to increase the protein in a simple meal.

SCALLOPED POTATOES

potatoes
onions
milk or stock
2 or 3 other vegetables such as:
tomatoes or carrots
beans or lentils (soaked and
    precooked)
cheese or nuts for the top

Slice potato and onion very thin. Make layers of these and the other vegetables. Barely cover with milk or stock and on the top layer sprinkle ground nuts or cheese.

Cook like a casserole, 1–2 hours at 325° (gas mark 3), covered. Uncover at the end to brown.

VEGETARIAN SHEPHERD'S PIE

red lentils
pearl barley
onion
garlic
carrots
walnuts
potatoes, steamed and mashed
cheese (optional)
Barmene or tamari (optional)

Simmer lentils and pearl barley until mushy. Add sautéed onion, pressed garlic, chopped carrots and walnuts. Cook until everything is tender. Top with mashed potato and place in oven. Cheese can be grated on top. Parsley or other herbs vary the flavour. Barmene or tamari can be used to season.

Serve with tossed salad or steamed greens.

Beans, Pulses and Tofu
(See also pp. 37, 39, and 41)

PASTA E FAGIOLI

350g/12oz wholewheat spaghetti
  or macaroni
100g/4oz dry beans (any kind or
  colour)
1 small tin tomato purée
1 onion
1 clove garlic
2 carrots and other vegetables to
  taste
basil and fresh chopped herbs
oil for frying
2–3l/3–5 pints water or stock
1 teaspoon salt
1 teaspoon sugar

Soak beans overnight. Cover with water or stock, bring to boil, skim, and simmer until almost done (1½–2 hours). In a large saucepan fry onion, garlic, tomato purée, salt, sugar, diced carrot and dried herbs and cook gently for about 10 minutes. Add 3 pints boiling water or stock, bring back to boil and stir in beans and (uncooked) pasta. Cook without the lid until pasta is done (15–20 minutes). Sprinkle with fresh herbs.

NUT CROQUETTES

1 cup ground peanuts
1 cup soft breadcrumbs
herbs and seasoning to taste
1 egg for binding (will work
  without this if necessary)
water for mixing

Mix the egg through dry ingredients, and moisten with water until slightly soggy. Let stand until it has absorbed all the water, adding more if necessary. It should be easy to roll into balls. Place on a floured plate and flatten. Coat with flour. Fry in oil.

COOKING SOYA BEANS

Soak beans overnight or longer. Discard water. Measure 2–3 cups water for every cup of soaked beans, and keep aside. Freeze beans for several hours. Bring to the boil in the water and simmer 1 hour. If you have no freezer, you will need to cook the beans for about 6 hours, or pressure cook for 45 minutes at 15 lb (1 kg) pressure. It is most important to soak soya beans and to cook thoroughly.

Tofu
(See also pp. 17 and 37)

Tofu (pronounced dough-fu) is the curd from the milk of pressed soya beans, formed into small squares. Because it is so cheap and such an excellent protein and iron source for vegetarians, it is really worth searching out a shop that sells it. Try wholefood shops or Chinese grocery stores; a pack to make your own can be found in some Japanese food shops. It will keep in the fridge for a week if you immerse it in a bowl of water and change the water daily.

The texture of tofu is rather like very firm junket, and it combines well with many vegetable dishes. If you are serving it warm it is best to fry it first on both sides in oil, or deep fry it and then add it to the dish. Beware of overcooking, though, as the texture changes, so add it to a dish not long before serving. It can also be served cold. To give some ideas, here are two recipes.

TOFU AND STIR-FRIED VEGETABLES

Serves 4

8 pieces tofu
root ginger
garlic
selection of vegetables
soy sauce

Fry the pieces of tofu in sesame oil until brown on both sides. Set aside. Add more oil to the pan and for extra taste some chopped root ginger and garlic. Then fry a selection of chopped/sliced spring onions, green pepper, aubergine, mushroom (dried have best flavour), peas, beans, leafy green vegetables, tomatoes. Stir-fry for a few minutes, then add some water to the pan (with cornflour to thicken if you like), soy sauce, seasoning (try star anise) and lastly the fried tofu. Simmer a minute or two longer and serve with noodles or rice.

TOFU SALAD

4 squares tofu
soya sauce
vinegar
oil
spring onions
root ginger

Cut the squares into small pieces
and toss in a dressing made by
mixing soya sauce, vinegar (rice
wine if possible) and a few drops of
oil (sesame is best – it's that which
is one of the distinctive flavours of
Chinese food). Add chopped
spring onions and a few slivers of
root ginger, chill and serve. Eat
with chopsticks!

Sautéing Vegetables

Raw vegetables are best but, if you are to cook, frying finely chopped
vegetables is an interesting method and a nutritious way to prepare a
meal. Pressure-cooking also preserves flavour and goodness. When
frying use vegetable oil and a hot pan (griddle, large frying-pan or
Chinese wok) over a fairly high heat. Many seasonings can be added
according to taste. In order to prevent burning, stir fairly continuously so
that each piece is gently cooked and the moisture and flavour sealed
inside. If you add stock or tomato juice, fry the vegetables first, add
liquid (not too much), bring to the boil, put on a tight lid and allow the
vegetables to cook themselves – simmering cooking time 5–8 minutes.

Fry any combination of these: carrots (cut into matchstick-size
pieces), finely chopped cabbage, finely chopped cauliflower, parsnips
(cut horizontally), onions, mushrooms, courgettes, peppers, marrow
(sliced), celery (in small chunks), apples. Serve with rice, omelettes,
grated Parmesan cheese or leftover grated Cheddar.

Grains and Seeds

Brown rice is a great staple. It can be cooked and eaten plain, fried with or without Chinese vegetables, or used in vegetable pies. Children enjoy pressed rice balls. Such rissoles can be bound with egg, flavoured with herbs, rolled in flour and refrigerated before use to help them cohere in the cooking.

BROWN RICE

Other whole grains such as rye, wheat or barley can be used or mixed with rice.

2 cups brown rice (long or short grain)
5–6 cups water, depending how chewy you like your rice*
1 tablespoon oil
salt and black pepper

Wash rice. Bring to boil water, oil and seasonings of your choice. Add rice, boil 2 minutes then simmer 20–25 minutes. Serve hot or cold. Add salt at the end.

Extras: bay leaves, mixed herbs, 1 clove, cinnamon, 2 garlic cloves, soy sauce, dried fruits (especially sultanas), tomato purée, pinch of cayenne pepper, or sugar.

*A good chew is not to be despised. Some research has shown that people feel well fed when their jaws have been exercised during a meal. Slimmers take note!

BUCKWHEAT AND MISO STEW

450g/1lb favourite stew vegetables (carrot, parsnip, onion or leek, etc.)
225g/½lb buckwheat
miso (a nutritious fermented soya bean product)
1½l/1–2 pints water or stock

Sauté the vegetables in a little oil until fairly well cooked. Add the water or stock, bring to the boil, cover and simmer gently for 10 minutes. Roast buckwheat on an oven tray for 10 minutes at 350° (gas mark 4) and add to stew. Simmer a further 20 minutes at least. The stew should be thick and mushy. When cooked, place miso in a bowl and mash in a little of the stew, then add this mixture to stew in the pot. Heat but do not boil.

MIXED GRAIN SALAD

Allow 125g/¼lb dry weight per serving and select at least 3 from the following in amounts and proportions of your choice:

brown rice (long or short grain)
long grain white rice
barley
whole rye grains
whole wheat grains
bulgar (or cracked wheat)
sweet corn (tinned won't need
  cooking)

Select at least one of the following to complement the grain protein:

bean or seed sprouts (see p. 62)
cooked green peas or broad beans
chopped nuts
sesame or sunflower seeds

Finally with an eye to colour and vitamins add any of the following:

green or red pepper
tomato
celery (for the crunch)
grated carrot
cress (any kind), parsley, other
  herbs
chives or spring onions
mushrooms

Each grain will take a different time, so treat each separately. Soak whole rye or wheat overnight. Wash and cook grains in plenty of boiling water. Add no salt until grain has absorbed all its water, or leave seasoning until you dress the salad. Expect any time from 8 minutes for white rice to up to 30 minutes or longer for whole grains. These can be prepared days ahead and kept in plastic bags in the fridge.

Prepare as appropriate in proportions and amounts of your choice. As a guide, use about 1 cup from this group to about 2 cups of cooked grains.

Mix all the grains in a big salad bowl, add the fresh vegetables at the last moment and dress with an oil and vinegar dressing. It will take a strong dressing if you wish, with olive oil, black pepper, mustard, pressed garlic, tarragon vinegar, a pinch of ginger, coriander or cardamom too if liked.

Sprouting Seeds

Fun for all the family and a job for the kids.

In as little as four days, in winter, we can obtain a food packed with goodness. With the sprouting process the level of many vitamins and minerals increases by 400–1300 per cent, especially vitamin C. The carbohydrate content lessens and the protein improves in value.

WHAT CAN YOU SPROUT?   Any edible seed intended for eating – not ones for planting. Easy and popular ones are mung and aduki beans, wheat, alfalfa and sunflower seeds. Any grain or beans should sprout and also seeds like poppy, sesame, fennel and fenugreek.

METHODS   Sprouting is easy. Use a naturally drained container (sieve, colander, etc.), or tie cheesecloth over the neck of a jar. Sprout only whole unmarked seeds, discarding those that don't sprout. Wash them well and soak overnight. In the morning rinse the seeds and place sprouting container in the dark, rinsing 1–4 times daily – soya beans, peas, sunflower seeds may need more frequent rinsing than, say, mung beans, lentils or the grains. Don't overfill the containers and rinse regularly and you'll avoid smelly seeds!

Individual seeds reach a peak for food value and palatability and then the values decline rapidly.

WHEN ARE THEY READY?   Wheat and sunflower (unhulled) – when the sprout is the length of seed; alfalfa, pea and soya – when 1–2 inches long; lentils – not more than 1 inch; sunflower – not longer than seed; mung bean – 1½–3 inches.

HOW TO USE SPROUTS

RAW in green or fruit salads – wheat and alfalfa are delicious raw.

SPROUTED WHEAT SALAD

1½ cup sprouted wheat
½ cup green onion chopped
½ cup celery chopped
2 avocados

Cube avocado and toss with sprouts, onions and celery. Serve on crisp lettuce leaves with lemon juice dressing.

COOKED as a garnish for soups, stews, in soufflés, etc. Blended into sauces, sandwich spreads, meat and nut loaves. Add at the last moment to preserve their crunchiness and nutritive value. Sprouts may also be added to bread mixes, egg foo yong and most cooked dishes and some desserts (poppy, sesame, anise, sunflower).

BEAN SPROUT SOUP

1½l/3pints stock, seasoned
2 cups bean sprouts
3 eggs, beaten
3 tablespoons parsley, chopped

Heat the stock, add sprouts and simmer for 3 minutes. Remove from heat. Stir in beaten eggs. Garnish with parsley. Serves 6.

Cooking times   Pea and soya: 15–20 minutes; chickpeas: 5–10 minutes; mung and aduki: need only a few minutes. Cooking is not essential for alfalfa, poppy, sesame, fenugreek, etc.

Egg and Cheese Dishes

COURGETTES WITH EGGS

450g/1lb courgettes
1 hardboiled egg per person
breadcrumbs
grated cheese (Gruyère, Edam or
   any cooking cheese)
500ml/1 pint liquid for white sauce
   made up of courgette water,
   milk and a tablespoon of sour
   cream or yogurt
1 tablespoon margarine
1 tablespoon flour

Wash the courgettes and cook in boiling water until nearly done. Drain. Depending on size cut them lengthwise or in slanting slices and place in buttered ovenproof dish.

Slice the hardboiled eggs in half lengthwise and place on top in a line down the middle, one up one down, or all face down, as you like.

Make a white sauce. Melt the margarine, stir in the flour, and season with salt and pepper and a little basil if liked. Add the liquid gradually, finally the cream or yogurt or some of the grated cheese (if you want a cheesier flavour). Pour the sauce over the courgettes and eggs in dish. Sprinkle breadcrumbs around the edge and grated cheese in the middle. For a non-vegetarian version a bacon rasher cut very small may be scattered over the top.

The dish may be refrigerated at this point, if it suits to prepare it ahead. In this case, heat through slowly for 1 hour when ready to use. Then, in both cases, sprinkle with grated cheese and cook for 10 minutes at 400° (gas mark 6) – or higher, if needed. When it is brown and bubbling (and the bacon cooked), serve. Goes equally well with pasta, rice or jacket potatoes.

EASY CHEESE SOUFFLÉ

Soufflés are not as difficult as their reputation would have. Start with this easy one.

5 eggs or 6 whites + 4 yolks
1 teaspoon salt
2 cups grated cheese
  (a combination of different
  cheeses gives a good taste as
  well as using up odds and ends)
6 tablespoons butter or margarine
6 tablespoons flour (try half
  wholewheat, half soy or
  experiment with different flours)
2 cups milk

Grate cheese. Turn oven to 300° (gas mark 2). Lightly grease a straight-sided casserole or soufflé dish. Melt the butter in saucepan. Add flour and milk to butter and slowly thicken like white sauce, stirring all the time. Add the egg yolks, well beaten. Add the cheese and salt. Mix and allow to thicken, using a low heat and a heavy saucepan for preference.

Beat the egg whites until stiff. Fold into the cheese mixture lightly with a wire whisk, or use an electric beater on lowest setting. Pour into soufflé dish. For a professional touch draw a circle on top about an inch inside the rim to give a ridged crust to your soufflé. Bake at 300° (gas mark 2) for 1 hour, sometimes a bit more or a bit less. Top should be medium brown. Do not keep opening the oven, particularly in the first 30 minutes. Serve immediately with a tossed salad. This is also good cold the next day.

You can make the cheese mixture ahead, and even keep it overnight in the fridge, or keep half of it and use it the next day with 3 egg whites. It is not a temperamental soufflé.

WHOLEWHEAT PANCAKES

2 cups wholewheat flour
2 teaspoons baking powder
1 teaspoon salt
3–4 eggs (separated if you've time
   and whites beaten until light)
2 cups milk
oil for frying

Sift the flour with baking powder and salt. Make a well in the centre, add beaten eggs and stir to a paste. Gradually add the milk (yogurt too if you have some to finish up) and use a whisk to get rid of the lumps.

Cook on a very hot greased griddle pan – make the pancakes any size.

Fillings:
grated cheese with tomatoes and oregano or purée of spinach;
fried mushrooms, leftover rice and seasoning;
any fruit purée – apple, apricot, fig;
or just honey and fresh lemon or orange juice;
or maple syrup;
or cottage cheese (with jam);
or spread one half with Marmite (or Barmene), the other with peanut butter (or tahini), and fill with bean sprouts, grated carrot and apple with raw onion (optional).

Pancakes can be prepared in advance and packed in silver foil to take on a classy picnic.

Alternative Second Courses or what to serve instead of pudding

After cheese and biscuits or fresh fruit, imagination seems to run dry. Here are some FIRST SALADS FOR TODDLERS which would be super served after a pasta dish, an egg meal, baked beans or cheese on toast.

1 Grate carrot on a very fine grater (for example a nutmeg grater). Add ½ teaspoon lemon juice mixed with 1 tablespoon cream or yogurt.
2 Cut up ½ fully ripe fresh tomato. Crush with a fork. Add ½ teaspoon lemon juice and 1 tablespoon cream or ½ teaspoon salad oil.
3 Put oil or cream or yogurt in a bowl and grate into it equal parts of fresh carrot and fresh apple. Stir and serve at once. Three-quarters apple and a quarter finely grated beet is a good mixture.
4 Finely chopped alfalfa sprouts with grated carrot, mixed with pineapple juice.
5 Mung bean sprouts and finely diced red sweet pepper, moistened with fresh orange juice.
6 Mashed avocado with grated carrot and lemon juice.
7 Finely shredded cabbage, diced apple and sultanas (soak in fruit juice first if at all dry), chopped if necessary. Dress with yogurt or a little unseasoned mayonnaise (just egg yolk and light oil).
8 Diced cooked potato, diced red and green pepper or red beet. Sieve a hardboiled egg yolk over and moisten with a little yogurt or oil.
9 (When the child can digest whole grains) Equal parts of barley (cooked), corn, mung bean sprouts. Dress with a little oil and top with chopped parsley (and chives).

More Alternatives to the Conventional Pudding

Divesting oneself of the prejudice that every meal must end with a sweet pudding is not enough if one's children remain victim to this harmful myth, or won't eat what you provide instead. Here are some more alternatives which may tempt them. Most are also suitable for children's parties. Most are finger foods (see also p. 25).

1   Mixtures of freshly cut fruit. If there are several children, start off with three things – say, bits of banana, apple and orange, all in a communal bowl. They help themselves with fingers or (if they can manage them) cocktail sticks.
2   Mixtures of fresh and dried fruit – apples and dried apricots, bananas and sultanas, prunes and fresh peach, apple and date, etc.
3   Mixtures of dried fruit (soak in orange juice if too dry and tough). Add a few chocolate drops or smarties for a treat, or crunchy granola (recipe p. 69).
4   Dried fruit and cream cheese. Stone prunes and fill with cream cheese (or better, soft white low-fat cheese). Figs and dates, fresh or dried, are good too.
5   Prunes (stoned) wrapped in bacon and then grilled are delicious, but retain the heat well, so be careful the child does not burn his mouth.
6   Squares of cheese on cocktail sticks with pineapple or apple.
7   Bread with margarine and hundreds and thousands. Cut into triangle shapes (standard Australian party fare).
8   Frozen ice lollies (or ice cubes) made with fresh juices, milk, yogurt (and honey to sweeten if necessary).
9   Half a banana frozen with a stick in it. Coat with melted chocolate before freezing for a special treat.
10   Cubes of pineapple on a stick may be dipped in honey, then ground nuts or shredded coconut, and then frozen.

MUESLI

2 cups muesli base (equal parts of rolled oats, jumbo oats, wheat flakes or bran, rye, barley or soya flakes, millet flakes or pearls and sesame or sunflower seeds)
½ cup raisins/chopped dates or apricots
½ cup coconut
½ cup chopped cashews/hazelnuts
¼ cup honey
2 tablespoons oil
1 chopped banana or peach
1 grated apple

Heat a griddle pan (cast-iron skillet or heavy pan) until it sizzles if you drip water on it. Put in oil and honey to heat. When honey is melted add all dry ingredients and slowly toss in oil and honey for 3 minutes. Turn heat off. Add fresh fruit. Serve with cream, natural yogurt, sour cream or milk.

Other uses
Muesli makes a good crumble topping on cooked fruit. Try substituting a proportion of muesli base in oatmeal recipes (for example those on pp. 86 and 87). You can add it to porridge for a hot breakfast – say, ½ oats, ½ muesli base. Add a few sultanas or currants instead of sugar.

CRUNCHY GRANOLA

4 cups rolled oats
2 cups wheatgerm
1 cup sliced almonds
1 cup sesame seeds
1 cup sunflower seeds
¾ cup brown sugar
½ cup safflower oil
½ cup water

Combine ingredients and bake at 350°/gas mark 4 for 1 hour, uncovered. Stir often till golden brown.
    Store in an airtight container.

Optional
1 cup coconut added now and then
2 cups raisins and/or chopped dried apricots added at conclusion of baking.

Other uses
Add 1 part granola to 2 parts crunchy peanut butter (or more until it all sticks together). Roll out and cut into squares between rice paper, or coat in coconut or sesame seeds. Store in the refrigerator.

FRUIT SALADS

Fruit salads are nearly always a welcome end to a meal, and good for one too, though for the sake of that part of the goodness involving vitamins try to prepare only 1 hour ahead. Almost any combination of fresh fruits work, so you can use dried or cooked fruits.

DRIED FRUIT SALAD

Prunes
Apricots
Apple rings (or freshly stewed apple pieces)
Peaches
Muscatels

Allow 50g/2oz per person (dried weight). Soak fruits and stew separately. They will take different times to cook until tender. Combine when cooked and allow to cool.

Serve with yogurt, cream or soft white cheese and meringues or coconut macaroons (see p. 90).

MIXED BERRY AND CURRANT KISSELI
(Cooked fruit salad)

Choose at least 3 from:
Strawberries
Raspberries
Blackberries
Bilberries
Cranberries
Lingonberries
Red- or blackcurrants
Rhubarb
2–3 tablespoons potato flour or arrowroot or cornflour in 3 tablespoons water
sugar to taste

Kisseli is fruit in a thickened but still liquid juice.

The juice will come from stewing any of the fruit that needs cooking (for example rhubarb) with plenty of water (avoid stewing strawberries or raspberries). One can use juice from bottled fruit.

Allow 50g/2oz of berries per person, and 600ml/1 pint of liquid per 500g/1lb of fruit.

Drain liquid into a pan, heat until boiling, then add cornflour already moistened with cold water. Stir well as you reheat until juice is thick. Remove from heat, add berries which do not require cooking, then other fruit.

RAHKOMENAKAKKU – Finnish Apple Cake

Cake base

¹/₂ cup margarine	Cream the margarine and sugar.
¹/₃ cup sugar	Add the egg gradually, and then
1 egg	the flour, sifted with the baking
1 cup flour	powder. Spread over oiled baking
1 teaspoon baking powder	dish about 25×20cm/10×8in.

Apple layer

2 cooking apples, or enough to cover cake base, or other fruit*	Slice the apples and arrange in rows, each slice slightly overlapping the one before, until the cake base is covered.

Soft white cheese topping

²/₃ cup soft white cheese	Mix the ingredients together in
1 egg	this order and pour over the apple
¹/₂ cup cream	layer, taking care to coat it all even
1 tablespoon sugar	if some pieces of fruit are not
1 teaspoon vanilla sugar	submerged.

Bake in preheated oven at 375° (gas mark 5) for 45 minutes or until done. Cut into squares when cool.

Note This cake does not keep well, but does freeze very well. Try making double quantity and freeze two-thirds. If you want to thaw it quickly, heat in a slow oven and serve hot – delicious for tea or as a dessert.

ORANGE QUARK TORTE

1 orange flavoured cake	Use a Victoria sandwich with the
250g/¹/₂ lb soft white low-fat cheese (*Quark*)	grated rind of an orange and about 1 tablespoon of juice added.
¹/₂ cup sugar (any colour) to caramelise	Bake in a torte shaped mould.
2 oranges or 4 satsumas	

Make the toffee by melting the sugar in a heavy pan over medium, then low heat. Stir all the time and remove from the heat just before a

*Other fruit may be used successfully in this recipe. New spring rhubarb or any currants work well. If you are fortunate enough to have some wild mountain berries like bilberries, lingonberries or whinberries, you will surely not regret using them to flavour this cake.

nice caramel colour is reached. It will get darker very quickly now, from the retained heat of the pan, even as you are pouring it onto an oiled tin tray. Choose something you can waggle in two hands for preference, and pour the toffee over it as thinly as possible. When cool (and hard), break into small pieces or powder with pestle and mortar.

On top of the cooled cake spread soft white cheese. This is the stuff known variously as *Quark* (in Germany), *fromage blanc* (in France), *ricotta* (in Italy), all akin to English cottage cheese, but only the smooth kind is suitable. Try making your own (see the recipe on p. 22). Whipped cream can be substituted.

Next decorate with segments of satsuma and/or cut pieces of orange.

Finally scatter caramel toffee on top. If you have been able to break oblique triangle shapes, stick them in standing up between the orange pieces for a pretty effect.

RHUBARB CAKE

A nice big cake for dessert or tea, when you are expecting a visiting family.

Crumble topping
125g/4oz SR flour
100g/3oz castor sugar
100g/3oz margarine
1 tablespoon water or flour for
   mixing

First prepare the crumble topping by sifting the flour into a mixing basin, adding castor sugar and rubbing in the margarine until a coarse crumb is reached. Add more flour if necessary or a little water if the mixture is too dry.

Fruit
350g/¾lb early rhubarb, green
   gooseberries or 3 sharp apples

Wash, trim and cut rhubarb into 1cm/½-inch lengths. Top and tail berries or peel, core and slice apples.

Cake base
200g/6oz SR flour
pinch salt
125g/4oz margarine
125g/4oz castor sugar
2 eggs
½ teaspoon vanilla essence
milk to mix

Cream the margarine and sugar until light. Lightly beat the eggs with vanilla essence and mix a little at a time into the creamed mixture, adding a little sifted flour and the salt along with the last few additions of egg. Fold in the remaining flour and sufficient milk to mix to a medium soft consistency.

Spoon the mixture into the base of a buttered 20cm/8–9-inch round tin (preferably with loose base or clipsided springform). Spread the mixture level. Cover surface with prepared fruit. Sprinkle over the crumble topping to cover the fruit completely. Place cake in the centre of a moderate oven (350°/gas mark 4) for 1–1¼ hours. Allow cake to cool before removing from tin.

HOMEMADE JELLIES

Any fruit purée or juice – except fresh pineapple – can be set with gelatine (follow instructions on packet). As such it makes a different texture for babies to enjoy, and provides some variety in the older child's diet – he may like ice cream or custard or yogurt with it.

PRUNE JELLY

225g/½lb dried prunes
brown sugar to taste
½ cup cold tea
small glass sherry or juice of a
    lemon
15g/½oz gelatine (1 envelope),
    soaked in a little cold water
a little less than 500ml/1 pint
    cooking liquid

Soak prunes overnight (or cook longer next day). Cook until they stone easily. Stone the prunes (purée some for baby). Retain the cooking liquid. Soak the gelatine. Place the prunes in serving bowl (a heatproof glass one, or jelly mould). In a measuring jug place cold tea and sherry or lemon juice, and make up to 500ml or a pint with cooking liquid. Adjust sugar if necessary.

Place the gelatine in a heatproof container in a pan of boiling water and stir until it is dissolved. Heat very gently if necessary, but never boil. Mix thoroughly with liquid in jug and pour over the prunes. Leave to set and place in refrigerator when cool.

Serve with whipped cream, yogurt or soft white cheese or custard.

HOT LEMON PUDDING

4 eggs
¾ cup sugar
grated rind and juice of 2 lemons
generous pinch of salt

Beat the egg yolks with salt and ½ cup sugar until light. Add the grated lemon rind and juice and stir well over a pan of hot water until thick.

Beat the egg whites until stiff and fold in remaining sugar. Fold into the lemon mixture. Pour into a buttered dish and brown lightly in a hot oven for 5–6 minutes.

SPANISH CREAM

15g/½ oz gelatine
500ml/1 pint milk
3 eggs
3 tablespoons sugar
¼ cup water
1 teaspoon vanilla

Dissolve the gelatine in water, heating slightly if necessary; never boil. Keep ½ cup milk, heat the rest to boiling, and stir in the dissolved gelatine. Beat together the egg yolks, sugar and rest of milk, and stir in the saucepan till thick like custard. *Do not boil.* Stir in stiffly beaten egg whites. Flavour with vanilla and pour into mould to cool.

CUSTARD ICE-CREAM

250ml/½ pint boiled custard (see p. 00)
125ml/¼ pint whipped cream
vanilla or other flavouring

When the custard is cool, cut the stiffly beaten cream through it, flavour and freeze in tray. Stir every half-hour until frozen.

PLUM-PUDDING ICE-CREAM

Soak ½ cup dried fruits in fresh fruit juice, rum or brandy, depending on the audience and the occasion. This is a good Christmas party dessert. Chop the fruit quite small and mix with the freezing ice-cream, adding spices of your choice.

POIRE BELLE HÉLÈNE

A pear half (peeled or not) with the pips removed is laid in a dish with a scoop of vanilla ice-cream on top. It is covered with hot chocolate sauce. Over it a few almond flakes are scattered.

Hot chocolate sauce In a thick saucepan melt 2 tablespoons of margarine. Add the same quantity of cocoa or carob powder and sugar. Stir for a minute then flavour with ½ teaspoon vanilla and add 2 tablespoons water, a little at a time and more if necessary, until a good consistency is reached.

PÊCHE MELBA

Fresh peach halves with a scoop of vanilla ice-cream on top are covered with fresh raspberry purée: 200g/6oz fresh raspberries blended and sieved to remove pips with juice of ½ lemon and sugar to taste. A few currants or other berries added will give depth of character to the sauce.

FRUIT SORBET

500g/1–1½ lb fruit (berries, pineapple or citrus fruit, the most suitable)
juice of ½ lemon
250g/½ lb sugar
¾ cup water
2 egg whites

Boil together the sugar with the water for 10 minutes. Let this syrup cool. Prepare fruit: crush berries, shred peeled pineapple with a fork, pulp oranges or lemons. Sprinkle lemon juice over and let stand in a glass or earthenware bowl. Add syrup when cool and 1 or 2 egg whites stiffly whipped. Turn mixture into freezer tray and stir every ½ hour until frozen.

FRUIT SALAD ICECREAM

1 can frozen concentrated orange juice
125 ml/¼ pint whipped cream
1–2 cups fruit puree made from:
a banana (and apple or pear)
125 ml/¼ pint fruit juice
1 tablespoon concentrated apple juice or honey

Whip cream until stiff, keep aside. In an electric blender combine the fruit coarsely chopped (peel can be left on apple or pear) with the fruit juice and concentrated apple juice or honey and liquidise. Mix in frozen orange juice and whipped cream and freeze.

NATURAL DRINKS

Caffeine, which causes the pleasant stimulant effect of tea and coffee, is widely recognised now as having harmful side effects. Children's cola drinks may also contain caffeine and the well advertised syrupy drinks wreak havoc on children's teeth.

There are many pleasant alternatives, however, which can help us cut down on – if not eliminate completely – our favourite cuppa! Dandelion and chicory coffees are increasing in popularity, as are herb teas like elderflower, chamomile, lemon balm, peppermint, etc. The great advantage of these natural drinks is that as well as being free of added chemicals they all have a gentle medicinal effect. Many of them both refresh and relax while others are rich in minerals and vitamins.

If you do drink a lot of tea a gentle way of cutting down is by adding a teaspoon of a herb such as peppermint, chamomile or mint in your normal pot of tea. Making proper herb tea is easy. Proceed exactly as for normal tea – adjusting quantities to taste for some of the stronger herbs.

Herbs Commonly Used Borage, lavender, rose petals, marigolds, thyme, catnip, mint, coltsfoot, woodruff, damiana, basil, aniseed, marjoram, raisins, ginger, sarsparilla, rosemary, sage.

A CHEERING WINTER TEA

1 teaspoon dried peppermint
  leaves
1 pinch ginger
1 teaspoon dried fruit
1 pinch aniseed
1 tablespoon elderflowers

This may be sweetened with a little honey.

Alternatives to Coffee Various roots and seeds may be used, roasted. They are freely available in the wild or may be bought in health food shops. 'Coffees' made from them are found even in grocers' – roots of comfrey, dandelion, chicory, burdock, carrots, etc., and seeds of cleavers, wheat, rice, acorns, etc. Dry roots or seeds in moderate heat and roast up as required. Before roasting, chop up the roots roughly into 5cm/2 in. lengths, then roast over moderate to high temperature till the root is a dark coffee colour.

ALTERNATIVE COFFEE

Use 4cm/1½ in. lengths of dried
   root
1 teaspoon dandelion roots
1 teaspoon chicory roots
2 teaspoons comfrey roots
1 tablespoon acorns, chopped

Roast the roots, etc., separately
till dark brown, and grind quite
coarsely. Simmer gently in milk
and water for 20 minutes or till the
taste is right. Sweeten with honey.

KARINA – BITTER-SWEET LEMON DRINK

Once the taste for this drink is acquired it will be found uncommonly
thirst-quenching, especially in hot weather. Children vary in their liking
for it.

2 lemons
1–2 tablespoons sugar or honey to
   taste
½l/1pint of boiling water

Slice the lemons thinly and place
in heat-resistant jug. Sprinkle
sugar on top and add the boiling
water. Leave the mixture to cool.
Drain before refrigerating (the
longer the lemon slices stay in, the
more bitter their skins will make
the drink).

For a treat try limes. They give a beautiful flowery taste.

For children's drinks, see pp. 26 and 104

SECTION III
CAKES, BISCUITS AND PRESERVES

Sweet things: How often

Most children like cakes and biscuits and most mothers provide them with these foods as they are convenient, instant and appreciated. We all like to see children enjoy their food, and what is wrong with that? Well, really only the sugar, or rather the degree to which the cakes and biscuits you serve are empty calories and sweet: you are helping your child adopt eating habits he'd be better without.

Empty calories do no harm if the child is already eating all he needs by way of nutrients each day and is metabolising them straight away in energetic play. But sugar does harm the teeth, and probably the heart (or more precisely the circulatory system), though again less harm is done if the calories are made use of in exercise.

So do question your family's need for cakes and biscuits. But, supposing you decide these foods have a place in your life (not necessarily every day, perhaps just at weekends, or when travelling, or when visitors come or something like that), here are some ways you can make them healthier and more nutritious. Try adapting these and your own recipes. Experiment and have fun.

For any query regarding weights and measures in the recipes, refer to the chart (pp. xi–xii).

Ways of Making Cakes and Biscuits Healthier

1   *SUGAR*

Use less sugar than the recipe says (some can be cut by half); try using brown or part white (or brown) and part honey. These sugars are usually interchangeable in recipes but honey is sweeter, so adapt on the scale of ⅔ cup of honey for 1 cup of sugar. It's also a good idea to reduce the liquid (if any) in the recipe and to add ½ teaspoon of bicarbonate of soda for each cup of honey. *(Sweet 'n' Low* – in the Book List – has lots more ideas.)

2   *FAT*

It is generally considered more important to reduce one's total intake of fat than to take sides on the controversial question of which fats are best. If you want to reduce animal and saturated vegetable fats in your diet, stick to margarines marked 'high in polyunsaturates' and use oils such as safflower, sunflower and arachide (groundnut). Most recipes will work using these; sometimes they hold together less well. In some cases nutmeats will provide an adequate fatty content – ground almonds, coconut, ground peanuts. A happy compromise for those unhappy about the manufacturing process of margarine, but still unsure about butter, is to blend equal quantities of butter and oil, store in the fridge and use for all purposes.

3   FLOUR

Try using wholegrain flour instead of white or instead of part of the white. Find the proportion that you can cook with easily and that your family likes best. Try enriching the flour component of the recipe with soya flour or wheatgerm to improve the protein content of your cake. *The Cornell Triple Rich Formula* for cakes and biscuits is: for each cup of flour called for, add first 1 tablespoon each of soya flour and powdered skim milk, 2 tablespoons of cornflour, 1 teaspoon of wheatgerm. Fill the rest of the cup with the flour of your choice, and baking powder if required. Use guide on baking powder container until you are happy judging the quantity yourself, then you can make your own.

RECIPE FOR BAKING POWDER

100g/4oz bicarbonate of soda
75g/3oz cream of tartar
25g/1oz tartaric acid

Roll out lumps. Sift into each other and mix thoroughly. Store in an airtight container.

4   EGGS

Free range eggs have more vitamin B_{12} than others. Wash them in warm water if need be (the shell is porous to cold water). Some people think that the number of eggs taken should be restricted to three or four a week for those on a low-cholesterol diet.

5   DRIED FRUITS

Most dried fruits are well endowed with minerals and enhance the nutritive value of cakes and biscuits to which they are added. They are also sweet and you can consequently lower the amount of sugar in the recipe. Wash them well to remove the liquid paraffin they have probably been stored in.

Cakes

TRADITIONAL VICTORIA SANDWICH

For each layer take one egg with equal weight of sugar, flour and margarine (about 60g/2oz).

Cream margarine and sugar. Add egg(s) one at a time. Fold in the sifted flour. Place in well oiled tin(s) (18–20 cm/7–8 in.) and smooth the tops. Bake in a preheated oven (350°/gas mark 4) for 25–30 minutes – depending on the size of the cakes. The top should spring back to a light touch when done; or test with a skewer – no mixture should adhere to it.

VICTORIA SANDWICH VARIATIONS

1   Fill with raspberry jam and whipped cream or lemon curd, and dust with icing sugar.
2   With fresh fruit: fill and top with cream (or soft white cheese). Decorate with pineapple, peaches, strawberries or any other berries.
3   Orange cake: mix into cake batter, before baking, the grated rind of an orange and a little juice. Ice with orange icing made with grated peel (½ teaspoon) and orange juice.
4   Adults will like – and children probably won't – a version with 1 tablespoon of instant coffee powder and 60g/2oz chopped walnuts, iced with coffee icing and decorated with walnuts. (Dad's birthday cake perhaps!)

All the above versions of the Victoria sandwich assume the traditional layer cake form. But you can vary the recipe again by using other moulds to cook it in. A torte shape with hollow top is useful, in fact, for 3 above. It can also be filled with fruit in jelly glazing. A ring shape, with or without kugelhopf-type ridges, is fun to use too. See Sections IV and V.

WHOLEMEAL FRUIT CAKE

500g/1lb wholemeal flour
pinch salt
1½ teaspoons baking powder
2 teaspoons mixed spice
1 teaspoon cinnamon
200g/6oz sugar (any colour)
200g/6oz dried fruit
2 beaten eggs
milk to mix (approx. 10
    tablespoons)
200g/6oz butter or margarine

If you like a moist cake, cover the fruit with water and bring to the boil. Remove from heat and let stand while you make the cake, draining before you add to mixture. (Keep this liquid for sweetening fruit juice.)

Sift dry ingredients together and rub in the margarine. Stir in the sugar and fruit. Mix in the beaten eggs and finally the milk (less is needed if the fruit has been soaked) to a dropping consistency.

Bake in a 20cm/8in. tin for 1¾ hours at 350°/gas mark 4.

MOTHER'S CHOCOLATE CAKE

3 tablespoons butter or margarine
2 tablespoons cocoa
1 cup sugar
2 eggs
1 cup SR flour
1 teaspoon vanilla
½ cup milk

Melt the butter and add the cocoa and other ingredients in the order given. Beat all together well. Bake in a greased and lined tin in a moderate oven (350°/gas mark 4) for 30 minutes or until done.

TREACLE PARKIN

In Yorkshire on Bonfire Night (5 November) parkin is one of the traditional foods, along with toffee apples. On other nights try it with stewed apple for dessert.

175g/6oz plain flour (any colour)
2 teaspoons baking powder
2 teaspoons ground ginger
100g/4oz margarine
350g/12oz medium oatmeal
50g/2oz brown sugar
450g/1lb syrup or black treacle
1 egg (beaten)

Grease the tin. Sift the flour, baking powder and ginger into a bowl. Rub in the margarine. Add the oatmeal and sugar. Melt the syrup (or treacle) but do not allow to become hot. Use this and the beaten egg to mix the dry ingredients together. Spread in tin (20×25 cm/8×10 in.). Bake at 350°/gas mark 4 until firm to the touch – about 1¼ hours. Cut into squares. Keeps well.

GINGERBREAD (no eggs)

350g/12oz flour (a mixture of soya,
     white and wholewheat)
100g/4oz demerara sugar
100g/4oz butter/margarine
85g/3oz blackstrap molasses
85g/3oz golden syrup
140ml/5 fl.oz milk
a few handfuls of
     currants/raisins/nuts
1 teaspoon each of ginger and
     mixed spice
1 teaspoon each of baking powder
     and bicarbonate of soda
1 dessertspoon vinegar

Sieve dry ingredients. Melt butter, molasses and syrup in the milk. Mix into dry ingredients and add dried fruits or nuts (roasted sesame seeds are good too). Dissolve soda in a little milk and add vinegar. Beat immediately into mixture. Pour into a well greased and lined loaf tin. Bake in a moderate oven (350°/gas mark 4) until a skewer comes out clean (about 40 minutes – 1 hour).

BANANA BREAD

3 *ripe* bananas
2 eggs (beaten)
225g/½lb flour
175g/6oz sugar
1 teaspoon salt
1 teaspoon bicarbonate of soda

Mix in bowl bananas and eggs. Sift together dry ingredients. Add to the first mixture (an optional extra – add ½ cup chopped nuts). Stir well. Put in greased loaf tin (23×12 cm/9×5 in.). Bake 1 hour at 350°/gas mark 4. Serve sliced and buttered.

COCONUT CARROT CAKE

2 cups brown sugar
1½ cups (corn) oil
2 or 3 eggs (beaten)
2 cups wholewheat flour
2 teaspoons baking powder
1 teaspoon salt
1 teaspoon cinnamon
1 cup chopped walnuts
1 cup coconut (fresh is unbeatable)
1 teaspoon vanilla essence
½ carrot (finely grated)

Mix the sugar with oil and beaten eggs. Blend the flour with baking powder and salt. Combine the dry and wet ingredients. Fold in the cinnamon, nuts, vanilla essence, coconut and carrot. Half fill 2 well greased and lined round cake tins, or 1 large loaf tin. Bake for 1 hour at 350°/gas mark 4.

Muffins and Drop Scones

CORN MUFFINS

¾ cup cornmeal (polenta)
1 cup flour
⅓ cup sugar
3 teaspoons baking powder
½ teaspoon salt
1 cup milk
1 egg (beaten)
2 tablespoons melted margarine

Mix the dry ingredients. Add the milk, egg and margarine. Mix and pour into bun cases. Bake at 425°/ gas mark 7 for 15 minutes or until done.

Serve split and buttered.

DROP SCONES

A favourite after-school snack and useful when friends arrive unexpectedly.

1 cup SR flour (or part wholemeal and 1 teaspoon baking powder)
¼ cup sugar
1 egg
a little milk

Combine in this order until a stiffish batter is formed. Heat a heavy iron pan and oil lightly (or use butter). Drop the batter on pan in tablespoonfuls, turn once, then keep wrapped in a cloth until all are made. It's best to butter the pan each time a new lot are put out.

For a special treat for children, make a little of the batter thinner so it will run in a stream from a pointed spoon and use this to write (in reverse) initial letter of each child's name on pan, cover with drop scone and cook as before.

Slices

GINGER ICED OATCAKE

225g/8oz rolled oats
2 level teaspoons ground ginger
100g/4oz soft brown sugar
100g/4oz margarine
2 level teaspoons golden syrup
a little melted fat or oil

Brush the tin very thoroughly with melted fat. Mix the rolled oats, ginger and sugar. Put the margarine and syrup into a pan and stir over a gentle heat until the margarine is melted. Mix this into the dry ingredients and pack it into the tin, levelling the surface. Bake in a moderate oven 350° (or gas mark 4) for 20–25 minutes.

Tin 18×28cm/7/11 in.

For the Topping
100g/4oz sifted icing sugar
50g/2oz butter
1 level teaspoon ground ginger
3 level teaspoons golden syrup

Topping: Stir all the ingredients over a gentle heat until melted. Pour onto oatcake, which need not be cold. Allow to set. Cut into triangles or squares when cold.

CAROB AND HONEY BROWNIES

½ cup butter/margarine/oil
²⁄₃ cup honey
2 eggs
1 teaspoon vanilla
½ cup carob powder or
2 tablespoons cocoa
¼ teaspoon sea salt
²⁄₃ cup wholewheat pastry flour
1 teaspoon baking powder
1 cup chopped walnuts (optional)
3 tablespoons milk

Preheat oven to 350°/gas mark 4. Cream the butter with the honey. Beat in the eggs one at a time. Beat in the vanilla and salt. Sift together the carob powder or cocoa, flour and baking powder and stir with nuts and milk into the batter. Turn into a well oiled or buttered 23 cm/9 in. square baking tin and bake 30 minutes or until done. Cut into squares while still warm. Remove from tin when cold.

OATMEAL BUTTER SQUARES

3 cups rolled oats (or 2 oats, 1 muesli)
1 cup brown sugar
7/8 cup melted butter
1 teaspoon baking powder
dash of salt
1/2 cup currants and orange peel (or other dried fruit) can be added.

Mix the rolled oats, sugar and baking powder in a bowl. Add salt. Pour over the melted butter and mix thoroughly. Pat mixture into an ungreased 20×30 cm/8×12 in. cake tin. Bake at 300° (gas mark 2–3) until golden brown (about 20–25 minutes) and cut into squares while hot.

BAKEWELL TART SLABS

Short crust
125g/4 oz wholemeal flour
1 tablespoon soya flour
40g/1½oz butter and extra oil (corn germ is good) to mix
About 1 tablespoon cold water
Jam to cover crust, any kind: raspberry, strawberry or plum.

Filling
2 eggs (separated)
1 tablespoon water
1 cup fresh breadcrumbs (try brown)
4 tablespoons sugar
50g/2oz melted butter
2/3 cup ground almonds
1 lemon (grated rind and juice)

You can use an electric mixer to make this short crust, or you can do it by hand. Sift soya flour onto wholemeal flour in a bowl, rub dobs of butter into the flour then add up to a tablespoon of oil gradually until a good crumb is obtained. Add water until it all coheres in one lump. Roll out and line a sandwich tin. Spread with warmed jam.

Beat the egg yolks with the water, and add dry ingredients, then lemon rind and juice. Fold in the egg whites beaten stiffly. Spread mixture evenly over lined tin and bake firm and lightly browned, for about 30 minutes at 425°/gas mark 7. Cut into slabs when cool.

For a recipe for Date Slices – see p. 109.

Biscuits and Meringues

CHAPEL ALLERTON CHOCOLATE DROPS

100g/4oz butter or margarine, softened
50g/2oz castor sugar (or demerara ground finer in a coffee grinder)
½ teaspoon vanilla essence
100g/4oz plain flour, less 2 tablespoonfuls which are replaced with cocoa or carob powder

Cream the butter and sugar with the essence until light and fluffy. Stir in the flour sifted with the cocoa. Drop 15–20 teaspoons of the mixture, well apart, on to an oiled baking tray. Bake just above centre at 375°/gas mark 5 for 17 minutes. Leave on the tray 1–2 minutes before transferring to a cooling rack.

ANZAC BISCUITS

100g/4oz margarine
1¼ tablespoons golden syrup
1 teacup SR flour
1 teacup rolled oats
½ teacup sugar
½ teacup coconut

Warm together in a saucepan the margarine and golden syrup. Put into a basin the flour, oats, sugar and coconut. Pour melted margarine onto the dry ingredients. Roll into small balls. Bake on an ungreased tray at 350° (gas mark 4) for 10–12 minutes.

MUESLI COOKIES

1½ cups muesli or substitute*
½ cup dried skim milk powder
½ cup wheatgerm (raw, toasted or mixed with bran)
¾ cup brown sugar or ½ cup honey
½ teaspoon salt
⅓ teaspoon ground cloves
1 teaspoon cinnamon
½ cup melted butter or oil
2 eggs

Mix together all the dry ingredients and spices. Add the oil and the beaten eggs (and the honey if used – measure the oil first, then the honey won't stick). Spoon onto a greased baking sheet. Bake at 350° (gas mark 4) for 12–15 minutes.

*You can substitute oatmeal (any kind), coconut or other ground nuts and dried fruit to taste. Some dried apricot cut finely is good. It also works using up to ½ cup of baby cereal in place of the muesli. Good finger food for children over 12 months. Make sure the fruit and nuts are finely chopped for little ones.

CRISPIES (Refrigerator Cookies)

125g/4oz butter or margarine
125g/4oz sugar (any kind)
1 egg (beaten)
250g/½lb SR flour
pinch salt (leave out for babies)
a little milk or yogurt for mixing
essence or flavouring according to
    version chosen

Cream the butter and sugar. Add the egg (some can be kept for glazing the biscuits), the essence or flavouring if required, and lastly the flour sifted with salt and any other dry ingredients. Bake in a quick oven (400°/gas mark 5–6) for 5–15 minutes according to thickness of biscuits.

1 *Peanut*   Use half peanut butter, half margarine. Roll the mixture into a sausage. If you are baking at once, slice sausage, glaze with part of egg and sprinkle finely chopped peanuts on top. If you prefer to refrigerate your mixture, coat sausage in chopped peanuts then wrap in tinfoil and keep in freezer. Wait until you have a hot oven and a spare ten minutes or sudden visitors, then slice as thin as you please and bake for as long as necessary (until edges of biscuits are starting to brown), 5–15 minutes.

2 *Orange or lemon*   Add a little orange or lemon juice to mixture, and a little (scrubbed and grated) fresh rind. Roll into sausage and coat with chopped crystallised peel. Then proceed as above.

3 *Coconut*   Add ½ cup of desiccated coconut to mixture, and roll in more on the outside. Proceed as above.

4 *Cinnamon Curls*   Use the basic recipe without added flavouring. Roll mixture out to ½cm/¼in thickness. Cover with cinnamon, then roll up like a small Swiss roll.

5 *Almond and buckwheat*   Substitute up to 4 tablespoons of buckwheat flour for part of the flour and add 2 tablespoons of ground almonds and 2 tablespoons of slivered almonds and a little almond essence. Proceed as above.

6 *Shapes*   The mixture may be rolled out on a floured board and cut with shaped cutters.

COCONUT MACAROONS

3 egg whites
1 cup sugar
$^1/_8$ teaspoon salt
1 teaspoon vanilla
$1^1/_4$ cups desiccated coconut

Beat the egg whites with the salt until stiff. Add the sugar, carefully folding it in. Pour vanilla onto the coconut and fold this in carefully too. When it is mixed, drop the batter from a teaspoon onto a greased and floured tin. Bake for about 30 minutes at 300° (gas mark 1–2).

Children generally like these. They improve a bowl of stewed fruit or almost any dessert from the point of view of both nutrition and taste.

MERINGUES

3 egg whites
6 tablespoons sugar

Beat the egg whites stiffly until peaks form, but do not overbeat. Fold the sugar in little by little, very gently. Prepare baking tray with brown paper covered with greaseproof paper. Drop mixture onto the tray, curling the spoon around to free it.

Bake at 200° (gas mark $^1/_4$) in a very slow oven until a hollow sound is heard when you tap your fingers on the meringues – they may take 2 hours. If they are getting too brown, turn off the oven and leave them in. If they are still not done, you can put them back again.

Preserves

Since shopping becomes more difficult with a young family, a well stocked larder is a boon. Children can help in gathering garden, farm or hedgerow fruits, and with the preparation, but the cooking is not a safe joint enterprise. It's interesting to experiment with low-sugar jams (see *Sweet 'n' Low* in the Book List). Ours involve the usual quantities. If you try less, keep the jam in the fridge or 'bottle' it as for preserved fruit.

BLACKBERRY OR ELDERBERRY JELLY

1 litre/1 quart elderberries or blackberries
1 litre/1 quart water
1 litre/1 quart crab apples or cooking apples
400g/1lb sugar per 500ml/1 pint liquid (see recipe)

Simmer the destalked berries in ½ litre/1 pint water till quite soft. Strain through a jelly bag. Chop the apples without peeling and simmer in ½ litre/1 pint water till soft. Strain through a jelly bag and combine both juices. Measure liquid and allow 400g/1lb sugar for every 500ml/pint of liquid. Boil juice in a preserving pan, add the sugar and boil for about 10 minutes or until set (see wrinkle test p. 92).

ROSEHIP JELLY

500g/1lb rosehips (wild rose are best)
1kg/2lb crab apples or cooking apples
600ml/1 pint water
500g/1lb sugar per 600ml/1 pint liquid
juice of 1 lemon

Simmer the hips in enough water to cover (approx. ½ pint) till tender. Add more water if necessary to prevent burning. Time depends on the hips – riper ones do quicker. When done, strain fruit through jelly bag. Cook apples as above. Combine both juices and measure to estimate sugar quantity (500g/1lb sugar per 600ml/pint liquid). Add lemon juice and boil juice, stirring in sugar till dissolved. Boil fast to set (wrinkle test p. 92). Pot into warm dry jars and cover while hot.

PRESSURE—COOKED SEVILLE ORANGE MARMALADE

Yield: seventeen 450g/1lb jars

2kg/5lb Seville oranges
3 litres/6 pints water
3 lemons
4·5kg/10lb granulated sugar

Wash and scrub oranges and remove stalk ends. Pressure cook at 15lb (1kg) for 15 minutes with half the water. When cooked, remove oranges and reserve liquid. Cut each one through the equator. Using a teaspoon, scoop out the pith and pips from the centre and place in a small saucepan. Add ½ litre/1 pint (⅓ of the remainder) of water to the pith. Bring to the boil and simmer for 10 minutes. Either chop the skins or put through a mincer. Put the chopped or minced peel into a large preserving pan with the cooking liquor from the pressure cooker. Add extra water to bring total water used to 3 litres/6 pints, including that used for the pith. Some water will have boiled away; do not add more to compensate.

Bring contents of the preserving pan to the boil slowly. Meanwhile, add juice from pips and pith through a strainer and the finely grated rind and juice of the lemons. As soon as the fruit is boiling stir in the sugar and bring back to the boil, stirring to make sure the sugar is dissolved. Boil rapidly till a set is obtained – about 20 minutes. Test a few drops on a cold saucer. It's done when you can push a wrinkle along with your finger nail. Remove pan from heat. Allow to stand 20 minutes, then ladle into warm dry jars. Cover and seal.

GLEDHOW PEAR AND GINGER CHUTNEY

2kg/4lb cooking pears
250g/8oz onions
900ml/1½ pints brown malt
  vinegar
750g/1½lb sugar
250g/8oz raisins
25g/1oz ground ginger
½ teaspoon each of ground mixed
  spice, dry mustard, ground
  cinnamon
1 teaspoon salt

Peel, core and chop pears finely. Chop onions very finely. Place both in an enamel or stainless steel pan with half the vinegar. Bring to the boil and simmer until tender and pulpy. Add the remaining vinegar, sugar, spices, salt and raisins. Stir until boiling and sugar is dissolved. Simmer, stirring occasionally, uncovered, until chutney has thickened (½–1½ hours). Pour hot chutney into hot clean jars. Seal when cold.

SECTION IV
CHILDREN'S PARTIES AND BIRTHDAY CAKES

The Menu

Good ideas are to be had in many books. For especially healthy ones see the books by Kenda and Williams, Vicki Lansky and Gena Larson in the Book List. Here are some of ours:

SAVOURY COURSE Little nibbly things are best and attractive presentation is likely to be appreciated, for example sticking cocktail sticks into an orange or grapefruit. On the sticks, pieces of cheese or ham and pineapple, prunes (pitted) wrapped in bacon and grilled (and cooled), meatballs (p. 46), pieces of sausage with green or red pepper and the like. (Further ideas p. 25 and pp. 67 and 68).

Kebabs (p. 44) are good party fare for children of all ages.

Sandwiches can be cut with pastry cutters into fancy shapes. Club sandwiches (3 or 4 layers) cut into inch square columns look fun. Open-faced sandwiches can be cut in triangles or other shapes. Try round faces: first cover bread with a spread (see pp. 36–8), make eyes from sultanas, hair from grated carrot, mouth from tomato, or what you fancy.

SWEET COURSE Again keep things small, especially for pre-school birthdays (there will come a time when they eat everything in sight), and don't have many things as kids tend to taste everything on offer. Cup cakes (p. 108) can be made in *petit four* cases, small meringues (p. 90) stuck together with ice-cream rather than cream.

The main item is, of course, the birthday cake (see p. 97 ff).

A bowl of sweets will always be enjoyed (p. 102). Watch the hands dive in.

DRINKS If you want alternatives to pop, try milk shakes (really frothy) or fruit cup (p. 104). Think of other adults attending – cider is easier to serve than tea. Provide straws for the children only if you are reconciled to their possible misuse.

The Guests

Keep numbers low, especially at first – for example, invite as many guests as the child has years. If your child wants to invite home a friend whose religion or health prescribes a special diet, do not dismay! The family will be used to the idea, so you needn't feel embarrassed in contacting them for information about what to give their child to eat. (The books on Special Diets in the Book List may be found helpful.)

Birthday Cakes

If you have three children and all birthdays are celebrated in the family with a cake, you will have made as many as forty birthday cakes by the tenth year of your marriage. Before then you will probably be looking for new ideas, though it sounds as though you should get a medal and be allowed to rest on your laurels!

A TREASURED RITUAL OF CHILDHOOD

Most children regard birthday cakes as very important. What turns a cake into a birthday cake? A plate on a stem makes any cake special; if you keep such a plate just for birthdays and if you go in for a good set of candle holders, you are halfway there. Special doyleys, paper ruffs around the cake and the like are all inedible signals that it's a birthday. Fresh flowers make a pretty decoration. This is what to concentrate on if you want to avoid over-indulgence in sugar and other junk foods. If you are prepared to say, well once in a while and just for special treats, then you will certainly delight the little hearts with gaudy jelly squares, hundreds and thousands, silver balls and any of the things in that part of the supermarket you usually try to steer them away from! A healthier decoration that some kids like is coconut. Fill a sponge with raspberry jam, cover with chocolate icing and sprinkle coconut over it and you have an Australian Lamington cake.

Usually one tries to make the kind of cake the birthday person wants or the flavour he likes best. But one can't consult the very young. Here are some ideas they should like. Don't feel you have to have a cake cake; a child on a special diet can get all the same fun from, say, half a watermelon or pineapple housing his birthday candles.

A theme is worthwhile for a child at four or five; before that it's really for you. (A younger child may well like to be consulted about certain details, however, such as the paper serviettes.) Our cakes are chosen with this point in mind.

First Birthday Cake: A rainbow cake (p. 99).

Second Birthday Cake: A marble cake (p. 98).

Third Birthday Cake: An ice-cream cake (pp. 99–100).

Fourth Birthday Cake: A caterpillar cake. Make it out of cup cakes, baked in a tin. This cake doesn't go on the cake stand, but winds its way along the party table. Its head is bigger than the other segments and has candles for antennae. Smarties, silver balls, etc., decorate the smaller segments iced in green, yellow or orange icing (made with orange juice and grated rind).

Fifth Birthday Cake: The novelty cake is really appreciated at this age. Some kitchen equipment shops will hire out cake moulds in special shapes such as numerals. We offer the hedgehog and the chocolate house (pp. 100, 101).

The quickest birthday cake ever: A chocolate snow Kugelhopf. Add 1–2 tablespoons cocoa or carob powder and 1 teaspoon vanilla to a 2-egg Victoria sponge (p. 82). Cook in a ring mould, preferably with fluted sides like a Kugelhopf. Cool on a rack for 10 minutes, then dust with icing sugar. Best eaten while still warm.

The trickiest birthday cake in the book: A Biscuit Birthday Card (age 6+). Use a Crispies recipe (p. 89) that you can roll out. With a sharp pointed knife cut out the letters for your message, for example HAPPY BIRTHDAY JOE or EVA IS SEVEN. Lift carefully, tearing around edges to detach the letters and bake. Stick on to a big card or board with a spot of icing, or, for a birthday trick, present them as a puzzle in a box for the birthday child to arrange himself. (An imprudent gift for a spouse who makes a speciality of anagrams, however!)

MARBLE CAKE

This cake uses only one egg.

125g/4oz margarine
125g/4oz sugar
1 egg
250g/8oz SR flour (or unbleached flour and 3 teaspoons baking powder)
pinch salt
⅓ cup milk
For each of the three portions:
1   ½ teaspoon vanilla
2   1 heaped dessertspoon cocoa or carob
3   a little cochineal colouring

Cream the margarine and sugar, add the egg and beat well. Add the sifted flour alternately with the milk. Divide the mixture into three equal portions and add a different flavouring to each (you may flavour the chocolate part with vanilla too, or add cherry or strawberry to the pink part). Place alternate spoonfuls of the three mixtures into a prepared 18cm/ 7-in. round tin. A ring mould is nice too, easy to make and cut.

Bake in a moderate oven at 350°/gas mark 4 for 45 minutes – 1 hour (a ring mould cake will cook quicker than an ordinary one). Decorate as you please (see above).

RAINBOW CAKE

Use Victoria sponge (p. 82) to make three layers: pink, chocolate and vanilla. Stick them together with whipped cream or soft white cheese and crushed fresh strawberries between the layers, or raspberry jam (warm, sieve and cool before spreading). Ice and decorate as you please. Suggestions:

(a) Simply dust with icing-sugar using a paper doyley as a stencil if you wish.
(b) Ice with a conventional icing in one of the colours used.
(c) A healthy frosting can be made by blending honey and cream cheese or soft white cheese until a good consistency is reached. Flavour with vanilla. Decorate with fresh flowers.

ICE-CREAM CAKES

Many variations on this idea are possible – ice-cream set in moulds, individual portions, big 'cakes', ice-cream in or on sponges and so on. Here are just a few ideas.

For the basic ice-cream use the recipe on p. 74 or the following one, which is less rich.

500ml/1 pint milk	Mix all ingredients in a pan and, as
1 egg	you heat, beat well with a whisk to
100g/3–4oz sugar	boiling point. Simmer for 3
2 tablespoons cornflour	minutes. Allow to cool, then
½ teaspoon vanilla	freeze. Whisk again when part
1 tablespoon butter	frozen (set around the edges).
	Before serving give it 15–30
	minutes in the ordinary part of the
	fridge.

ICE-CREAM RABBIT (or other mould shape)

Line mould with oil and toss coconut around to stick to all sides. Place in freezer to cool while you make a vanilla ice-cream – or flavour of your choice. When the ice-cream is frozen, remove, whisk quickly, fill mould, and refreeze. Remove again, plunge into hot water for a moment, and turn out onto a plate which will fit into your freezer. Decorate or paint with homemade dyes (p. 100). Refreeze.

HOMEMADE DYES

Beetroot (pink)
Parsley or spinach (green)
Carrot or orange peel (yellow)

Squeeze the vegetable in a gauze bag or through a very fine sieve to make juice. Paint with a clean paint brush.

ORANGES AND LEMONS

Sorbet is not very good at holding a shape on its own, but delicious if served in fruit cases (see recipe p. 7). Oranges have lids cut off and pulp scooped out, or are simply cut in half.

CHOCOLATE HEDGEHOG

A 2-egg Victoria sponge (see p. 82)

Bake in a greased and floured 20cm/8in. sandwich tin for 20–25 minutes in a moderate oven (350° or gas mark 4) until firm.

Butter cream and Decoration
125g/4oz butter
250g/8 oz icing sugar
25g/1oz cocoa
125g/4oz slivered almonds
3 smarties

Cream butter and beat in sieved icing sugar and cocoa. Sandwich two cake halves together with a little butter cream, place cut side down on a flat plate and shape one end to a point for nose. Ice cake with the rest of butter cream and mark with a fork.
Decorate with almonds for spines, 3 smarties for eyes and nose.

Chocolate Hedgehog

CHOCOLATE HOUSE

A 3-egg Victoria sponge (p. 82)
flavoured with:
25g/1oz cocoa and
1 teaspoon vanilla essence

Butter icing and Decoration
170g/6oz butter
340g/12oz icing sugar
50g/2oz plain chocolate
2 eating apples
lemon juice
marshmallow

Cream the butter and sugar.
Gradually beat in the eggs. Fold in
the sieved flour and cocoa. Bake in
2 greased and lined 15–18 cm/6–7
in. square sandwich tins at 375°
(gas mark 5) until firm. When cool
cut a 5 cm/2 in. slice from each
square for the roof.

Cream the butter and beat in
icing sugar. Take out 3
tablespoons for piping. Add the
melted chocolate to the remainder
and beat well. Sandwich the cakes
together with icing to form a
house. Place smaller pieces on top
for roof. Cover entirely with
chocolate icing. Pipe white icing in
the shape of door and window.
Sliced apples dipped in lemon for
roof. Make a marshmallow
chimney.

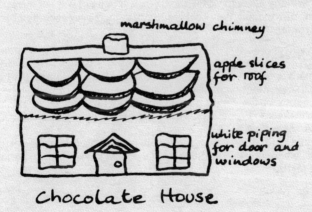

marshmallow chimney

apple slices for roof

white piping for door and windows

Chocolate House

The Bowl of Sweets

THE BOWL-CEREMONY AS A SUGAR SUBSTITUTE

As with the birthday cake loving care and attention can be spent on wrappings if you are seeking to minimise the consumption of empty calories, so put each child's sweets in some container, and put fewer sweets and more in the way of balloons, hats, party whistles and the like. You may choose to give the party pack as a parting gift and such a ceremony will compensate, too, for the more usual party ritual of nothing but sugar. Indeed, you could give special fruit instead of sweets – get small cheap baskets and fill with fresh strawberries, grapes, satsumas, dried fruits. Otherwise your container might take the form of a Dick Whittington swag on a stick – use paper serviettes if you don't want to run to real spotted handkerchiefs. Cheap calico or gingham can be made into bags – names can be written on in wax crayon and ironed in. Christmas crackers can be made from the cylinders inside paper rolls, other boxes can be collected and your child could help make them into ship-shaped party packs, little trains or his own invention. Ceremony can be introduced as well in the way sweets are come by. They may be prizes, they may be hidden and found (try a hunt for wrapped Easter eggs in the garden), they may be released on discovery of a password. Start your mind working along these lines and you will think of ways of increasing the fun surrounding the sweets rather than increasing their number or sugar content.

THE SWEETS

Alternatives to commercial sweets apart from fruits fresh and dried and various suggestions on p. 68 may be found in popcorn (home popped is fun), honey in the comb, and small biscuits like iced gems, ratafias, savoury shapes, Chinese prawn crackers and, of course, homemade sweets (see recipes p. 103).

Should you decide that some commercial sweets are inevitable, favour, where possible, those without dyes and kinds which do not stick to the teeth.

TURKISH DELIGHT

½ cup boiling water
2 cups raw sugar
2 tablespoons gelatine
½ cup cold water
½ cup orange juice
¼ cup lemon juice
raw sugar powdered in an electric
   blender or icing sugar

Place the boiling water and 2 cups
sugar in a heavy pan and heat,
stirring well until the sugar
dissolves. Continue to boil,
without stirring, until the mixture
registers 225° on a jam
thermometer or spins a thread.
Meanwhile soak the gelatine in
cold water, then add to syrup with
orange and lemon juice. Put
through a fine sieve. Pour into a
chilled pan 2·5 cm/1 in. deep.
Allow to stand until the mixture is
firm. Cut into small squares and
coat with icing sugar. Doesn't
keep well.

SESAME SEED BRITTLE

2 cups brown sugar
2 cups sesame seeds
1 teaspoon vanilla

Alternative: Substitute 1 cup
   granola or ½ cup sultanas for
   part of the sesame seeds

Place the sugar in a heavy iron
skillet and heat gradually, stirring
constantly until the sugar melts
and forms a golden syrup.
Remove from heat and stir in the
seeds and vanilla. Pour mixture
onto a buttered oven tray,
heatproof platter or marble slab.
Spread into a thin layer. Cool.
When cold break into small pieces.

APRICOT AND DATE BALLS

½ cup dried apricots (soaked in
   fruit-juice)
½ cup pitted dates
honey to taste
1 cup coconut

Leave the apricots to soak in fruit
juice of your choice overnight.
Purée the dates and apricots and
add honey to taste. Roll in
desiccated coconut to form small
balls 2·5 cm/1 in. in diameter.

AUSTRALIAN FRUIT CUP

Fruit base
1 small pineapple (or tin of
   crushed pineapple)
juice of 2 oranges
2 more oranges diced
1 grapefruit
1 lemon
sliced banana

Optional/seasonal extras
1–2 passionfruit
100g/4oz strawberries (halved)
½ cup sliced cucumber
6 mint leaves (or borage)

Before serving add
ice cubes (1–2 trays depending on
   the weather and numbers)
2 bottles lemonade or 1 lemonade
   and small tonic and small dry
   ginger

For adults or teenagers add
1 bottle cider
1 cup cold tea

Peel and shred the fresh pineapple
with a fork (or empty the tin) into
a punch bowl. Slice the banana
and cover with orange and lemon
juice. Halve the grapefruit and
dice, squeeze the juice of other
half and add both. Dice the two
oranges and add to the mixture. (If
it is a big party lasting a while and
you want to pep the cup up when it
runs out, add more cut fruit and
fizz). Add the optional/seasonal
extras and leave to stand an hour
or more to let the flavours blend.

Before serving add the ice and
fizz.

The number this will serve
obviously depends on the thirst of
your guests and the length of the
party. It can be scaled down or
scaled up as you wish.

SECTION V
COOKING WITH CHILDREN

HOW TO MAKE THE PROJECT WORK

Somewhere between the ages of 2 and 3 most children really love to help in all household work. It is nice for them to be able to do so, and an important formative influence on their attitudes to household tasks and pleasures. Therefore, as well as having fun, and as well as learning lots of things about the chemistry of cooking, the way various materials behave, the feel of rubbing fat into flour, attitudes to food in the family, and the taste of things at different stages of making, children are learning how to co-operate with someone else in a joint enterprise and gaining the pleasure of providing for others something they will enjoy eating.

There are only a few recipes in this section specially adapted for making with children, but many more throughout this book in which a child can participate. Check it through first. Avoid recipes involving such things as pans of hot oil or syrup, recipes which are in any way tricky. (Failure is very disappointing to a child; make sure – or as sure as you can – that his effort will be rewarded with success. There will be enough accidents to ensure he does not get a mistaken impression of reality!) Avoid recipes with expensive ingredients which he could ruin. There are not many recipes like this here, so you should be able to find plenty suitable. Check that there are jobs in it that the child will enjoy doing, and that the result is something he will enjoy eating and sharing with his friends or family.

See Doreen Chetwood, *Young Cooks in the Kitchen*, and other titles in Book List, for more ideas in this area.

MAKING THE RECIPE UP

You will have to decide when your child is old enough or competent enough to move from plastics and wooden non-breakable equipment to china, pyrex and the like. You will have to decide when he can handle a knife, open a can, stir a hot saucepan over heat, get a tray out of the oven. By the time he is 9 or 10 he is likely to be quite a good cook doing most of these things, even earlier maybe, but it's for you to help produce this result by your guidance over what is right at what point in his development, given how skilful or clumsy he is likely to be. As with most dangers there are several dimensions to the problem: danger to the child of a more or less serious kind, danger to things (breaking bowls, etc.), danger to the thing cooked (probably the least serious). He will feel rotten about it anyway if he spills or spoils the food, so don't shout or scold for *that*. To help you keep calm and cheerful (so you don't shout despite yourself), here are some ways to set up the situation that will make the possibility of failure less likely.

1 Children get to a stage where they like to help sooner than they are able to be a help. Don't let them rush you into a cooking spree before you have worked out what their contribution will be.

2 Think which jobs the child is going to be able to do and in what order and whether there will be a break when he can run off to be called back for a more exciting moment. Most recipes require more concentration than a young child is capable of.
3 Have ingredients ready to go – anything to chop, chopped; butter warmed; flour measured.
4 Organise yourself so you don't have to turn your back on him. It is a good idea all the same to have a work surface out of his reach where you can place equipment he might fiddle with when it is not being used.

JOBS CHILDREN LIKE TO DO

1 Cracking eggs and breaking eggs.
2 Sifting flour in a sifter.
3 Stirring and tasting.
4 Turning egg beater handle (not usually competent till 5–6 years old).
5 Brushing pastry with egg or milk (for example making mince pies at Christmas).
6 Rolling out pastry and cutting with shapes.
7 Greasing or oiling tray or cake tins.
8 Weighing or measuring into a measuring jug (around 4 years).
9 Decoration of iced cakes.
10 Washing up afterwards of unbreakable things used.

Be lenient with incompetence. Try doing the job with your left hand if you want to appreciate how much more difficult it is for the child's untrained hand.

JOBS THE PARENT SHOULD DO

1 All work with sharp knives. When your child has started to use a knife at table, give him a butter knife to chop up something easy like cheese or fruit.
2 Work with other sharp instruments, scissors, graters, skewers, etc. Mouli-graters, mouli-sieves, mincers and the like with handles to turn may attract offers of help. Keep a close watch if you allow him to try.
3 Electrical equipment, mixers, blenders, etc., should be controlled by the parent. At a certain stage the child will be able to turn the switch on and off for you, sift flour into the mixer, etc. But be present *all the time* he is helping. Turn it off even just for a moment if you are reaching away, turning your back, checking how something is doing or whatever. Be sure he understands the dangers involved.
4 Keep the child well away from the cooker when you open the oven door. Hold him up to see when you have your hands free.

SIMPLE GERMAN APPLE CAKE

100g/4oz margarine
½ cup sugar (or brown sugar)
2 eggs
1 cup SR flour (or brown flour and
   3 teaspoons baking powder)
1–2 apples
cinnamon to taste

Cream the margarine and sugar (the child can have a stir, but won't be able to do the job without practice). Add the eggs (let him crack them gently; later he will learn how to open them too) and mix after each one. (Let him have another stir while you measure the flour, if this is not already done.) Add the flour (the child may be able to operate a sifter, which is actually *a help* as you can stir it in using two hands).

Now the mixture goes into the tin, which the child may have greased. It is best to line it too with greased paper. Sprinkle cinnamon over the top (or supervise the sprinkling). Then slice the apples (taking care to keep the knife out of his reach). The child's job is to poke the slices into the cake mixture, leaving the ends sticking up. If you like lots of apple you can fill all the space available. As long as each piece has some cake mixture around it, the cake will rise.

Bake in an oven preheated to 350° (gas mark 4) or a little quicker for 30 minutes. The more apple the longer it takes, so you may have to leave it longer. Test with a skewer.

Serve hot with yogurt for dessert. If you are out of apples try adding the grated rind and juice of an orange instead. This is delicious hot.

CUP CAKES

Use the Victoria sponge recipe (p. 82). Add chopped dried fruit, cocoa and vanilla, grated lemon or orange rind and juice, or whatever is considered nice in your house. Let the child help make up the recipe. He will also like separating the cake cases and setting them out on a tray. You are quite likely to get in a fearful mess if you let him fill (or rather not more than half fill) them, but he needs to practise some time. He will learn by watching, if willing, and see how you fill a teaspoon and then push it into each case. Separate the different aspects of the task: first he may fill the teaspoon and you put it into the case. When he shows competence in that, let him do the messy bit he's been dying to do, but help each spoonful *into* its case.

Bake in a moderate oven, 350° (gas mark 4), 10–15 minutes. Ice when cool. The child can decorate the cup cakes. If you are using *petit four* cases cook for a shorter time.

DATE SLICE

100g/4oz margarine or oil
100g/3–4oz sugar (any colour)
1 egg
1 cup flour (any kind)
1–2 teaspoons baking powder
¾ cup chopped dates
½ teaspoon vanilla

Cream margarine and sugar. The child has a go too, then you give him the egg to crack. He can break it into a little plastic dish so bits of shell can be removed before it is added to the mixture. When the egg is mixed in, sift in the flour. The child can work the sifter while you hold the basin and stir. Add vanilla and dates.

The child can oil a baking tin (about 15×23 cm/6×9 in.). Spoon in the mixture and press flat. Bake in a moderate oven 350°(gas mark 4) 25–30 minutes. Ice while warm with vanilla icing if liked.

Connoisseurs' Omelettes

A child of 10 or so might like to make a meal for everybody. Omelettes are a useful thing for him to learn, with adult help the first time at least. Here are some tempting flavours for him to offer on his menu along with the more usual cheese, ham, mushroom. Jam can be offered to a sweet-toothed member of the family.

1　TURKISH ROSE OMELETTE

4 eggs
½ teaspoon celery salt
pinch marjoram
½ cup clean petals from freshly picked roses, plus a few more for garnish

Break the eggs into a blender. Season. Add rose petals and blend at medium speed until eggs are fluffy and petals almost liquefied. Pour the mixture into a greased pan and cook over medium heat. If the heat is right the top will be just set when the bottom is browned. Fold the omelette and slide onto a plate. Sprinkle with paprika and petals – exotic!

2　BEANSPROUT OMELETTE

4 eggs, lightly beaten
2 tablespoons water
sea salt and black pepper
1 cup beansprouts (p. 66)
1 tablespoon chopped parsley

Combine eggs, water, salt and pepper in a bowl. Heat some oil in a heavy pan, pour in mixture and stir until it begins to set. Leave it cooking gently until it is just set, sprinkle with sprouts and parsley, and fold over and serve.

3　OMELETTE AUX FINES HERBES

Use recipe 2, but instead of beansprouts add chopped chervil or parsley, thyme or marjoram and chives, 1 tablespoon per person.

4 OMELETTE BASQUAISE

In a separate saucepan fry gently in olive oil (per serving 1 tablespoon each of) finely chopped onion, green or red pepper and tomato. Add a little basil or a scrap of garlic. When nearly soft and blended make your omelette (recipe 2), pour over the omelette when cooked, fold and serve.

Make a note here of your own favourites and successful experiments

Simple Meals for Young Cooks

CRISP CHICKEN AND LOW-FAT CHIPS

Buy chicken pieces or joint a chicken (with help if necessary), allowing a piece per person. In a flour bag place 2 tablespoons of flour, bran or oatmeal with pepper and salt. Brush chicken pieces with milk, drop into bag, and shake about to coat. In a pan with a little oil brown quickly on both sides. Place in a single layer in a baking dish. Bake at 325°/gas mark 3 for about 10 minutes, then turn heat up to 400°/gas mark 6 and keep chicken low in the oven. On an oiled tray spread frozen chips sprinkled with a few drops of oil and bake in the top of the oven for 20–30 minutes. Swap places with the chicken if necessary to get both things brown and cooked together. Fresh chipped potatoes can be used. Allow a little longer, and turn several times while cooking.

OLD-FASHIONED MACARONI CHEESE

250g/8oz (brown) macaroni
2 tablespoons butter or margarine
1¼ cups diced cheddar cheese
500ml/1 pint milk
½ teaspoon salt
¼ teaspoon pepper
2 eggs beaten
breadcrumbs for topping

Cook the macaroni till not quite soft. Heat oven to 350°/gas mark 4. Combine macaroni, butter, cheese and pepper and salt in a greased baking dish. Mix eggs and milk together and pour over macaroni. Sprinkle a little paprika (optional) and breadcrumbs over the top. Bake 40–50 minutes.

SARDINE CONK

1 tin of sardines, sild or brisling
juice of ½ lemon
pepper and salt
chopped parsley (optional)
slices of toast cooked on one side
    (rye or wholemeal taste best)

The name was invented by a 2½-year-old. He used to help get the tin out of the box. You open and hold the tin and the child gets the fish out with a fork and mashes them in a bowl with lemon juice, seasoning and oil from the tin. Spread on uncooked side of the toast. Brown lightly under grill and serve.

PLAY DOUGH

For times when it is not suitable for your child to participate in your cooking keep a supply of play dough. With it, depending on the child's preferences, offer a rolling pin and cut-out shapes (many plastic toys will make patterns or cut shapes; so will yogurt pots and such-like) or modelling tools – though this play dough tends to be too soft for stand-up sculptures – or little cars to get stuck in the bog and a crane to drag them out again, or pebbles, buttons, little sticks (for example used matchsticks with burnt end rubbed off) to make decorated birthday cakes for the dolls.

The child could help with the mixing, but not the cooking part.

4 cups plain flour 4 cups water 2 cups salt 2 tablespoons cooking oil 100g/4oz cream of tartar food dyes (optional) or paint powder	In a heavy saucepan mix ingredients together to make a sloppy mixture. Cook over gentle heat stirring all the time for 15 minutes. It will get harder and harder to stir as it gets stiffer. When it becomes translucent and coheres together in one lump it is done.

If you are using dyes to colour the play dough it is fun to add them at the end and just mix a little for a marbled effect. It looks pretty to use several toning colours – for example blue, yellow and green – which will eventually become uniform green, of course. The child will see how colours combine to make others. Will keep in an airtight container for up to 6 months.

FACTORY BREAD PLAY DOUGH

Simply knead factory bread into a ball. If too dry, add a little paint to moisten and colour it. It can be painted when dry.

Beyond Cooking with Children

If you would like to involve your child with the decisions and procedures to do with food in the house, here are some ideas. One reason might be that despite your wish to the contrary the kids have food fads. Coming at the problem from another direction may prove the best approach (though it needn't be a way connected with food).

1 **GROWING FOOD** From beansprouts (pp. 62–3) or windowsill gardening to a row in the family vegetable patch there are plenty of ways for a child to be involved, even if she only helps choose what the family should plant (see also the books on growing your own food in the Book List).

2 **KEEPING ANIMALS** Why not a hen instead of guinea pigs, or a goat instead of a dog? As well as the pleasure and responsibilities of a pet, there is the bonus of food (see NCAT Pack, p. 117).

3 **PICKING FRUIT** (See preserves pp. 91–3). Children enjoy such tasks, whether in your own garden, a friend's orchard, a farm open to the public or a country ramble gathering berries or nuts (more ideas in Richard Mabey, *Food for free*, Fontana).

4 **FISHING** If someone encourages your child in this hobby be grateful! A seashore walk may produce shellfish and other goodies for the less skilled.

5 **BECOMING VEGETARIAN** A likely time for a child to make this choice is the period from 5 to 9 years when compassion for animals is often deeply felt. Teenagers are perhaps more concerned with the wise use of the world's resources. Be sympathetic to the social pressures the child feels and be patient (whichever side of the fence you hope she'll end up on).

6 **SHOPPING** Make a game of 'hunt the additive-free foods' in supermarkets, 'spot the rip-offs', and other consumer sports of your own invention.

7 **MENUS** A project for any child over, say, 7 and an instructive exercise for a fussy eater is to design a week's menus for family meals. You have to promise to make and eat them. You may need to complicate matters with a cost limit.

8 **TV** How is food presented? What do they think of the advertisements? Why are some foods advertised more than others?

REFERENCES, BOOK LIST, AND ADDRESSES

ON DIET IN PREGNANCY

NCT leaflet,* *What to eat during pregnancy and afterwards* (L15).

T. K. Basu, *Growing Up Healthy, a nutritional guide for mother and child* (Thorsons Publishers Ltd, 1971).

Phyllis S. Williams, *Nourishing Your Unborn Child* (USA, Avon).

ON BREASTFEEDING

Sylvia Close, *The Know-how of Breastfeeding* (John Wright and Sons, Bristol).

Penny and Andrew Stanway, *Breast Is Best* (Pan).

NCT leaflets* particularly recommended:

   Ante-natal advice for mothers keen to breastfeed (L31).
   Care of the breasts and nipples (L21).
   Introduction to breastfeeding (L24).
   More about breastfeeding (L25).
   Easy breastfeeding (L4).
   How to express and store breastmilk (L22).

ON FEEDING BABIES

NCT leaflet,* *Introducing solid food* (L27).

Adelle Davis, *Let's Have Healthy Children* (Unwin Paperbacks).

Sylvia Hull, *Cooking for a Baby* (Penguin).

M. E. Kenda and P. S. Williams, *The Natural Baby Food Cook Book* (USA, Avon).

Vicki Lansky, *Feed Me! I'm Yours* (USA, Bantam).

Gena Larson, *Better Food for Better Babies and Their Families* (Connecticut, Keats Publishing Inc.).

Penelope Leach, *Babyhood* (Pelican), for advice on feeding problems.

Brenda O'Casey, *Natural Baby Food* (Duckworth).

Open University Course Material, *The First Years of Life*, Book 5.

Innes Pearse, *The Quality of Life* – the Peckam approach to human ethology (Scottish Academic Press).

ON BREADMAKING

Edward Espe Brown, *The Tassajara Bread Book* (Berkeley, Shambhala Publications Inc.).

Rita Davenport, *Sourdough Cookery* (Bantam).

Elizabeth David, *English Bread and Yeast Cookery* (Allen Lane/Penguin).

*NCT leaflets may be obtained from your local branch or from Headquarters (9 Queensborough Terrace, London W2 3TB), who will send a complete list of titles on request. See also *Pregnancy and Parenthood*, edited by Anne Loader on behalf of the National Childbirth Trust (OUP).

ON COOKING AND NUTRITION GENERALLY

Sheila Bingham, *Nutrition, Better Health Through Good Eating* (Corgi). Unless otherwise specified most nutritional information in this book comes from Sheila Bingham's very sound and well informed work, originally published as *Dictionary of Nutrition* in 1977. It is particularly useful in paying attention not only to the nutrients in foods, but to whether and how we can best digest them.

Sharon Cadwallader and Judi Ohr, *Whole Earth Cook Book* (Penguin).

Complete Guide to Calories (Slimming Magazine).

Peter Deadman and Karen Betteridge, *Nature's Foods* (Unicorn Bookshops).

The Eco Cook Book (Southampton Friends of the Earth, 24 Ferndene Way, SO2 4SZ).

The Frugal Cook Book and *Frugal Soya* (Global Village Crafts, South Petherton, Somerset).

Jean Hewitt, *The New York Times Natural Foods Cookbook* (USA, Avon).

Frances Moore Lappé, *Diet for a Small Planet* (NY Friends of the Earth/Ballantine). A seminal work on changing eating habits and a key reference on complementing proteins.

James L. Mount, *Food and Health of Western Man* (USA, Halsted Press; UK, Precision Prèss).

The Penguin cookery series provides a variety of reliable and interesting books on many aspects of cooking, including the useful *Penguin Cookery Book* by Bee Nilson.

Irma S. Rombauer and Marion Rombauer Becker, *Joy of Cooking* (USA, Bobbs Merrill).

Sweet 'n' Low – simple snacks, cakes, drinks and healthy things using little or no sugar (Friends of the Earth, Birmingham, 54–7 Allison Street, Birmingham 5).

Colin Tudge, *Future Cook, a Taste of Things to Come* (Mitchell Beazley).

ON SPECIAL DIETS

Bee Nilson, *Cooking for Special Diets* (Penguin).

Hilda Cherry Hills, *Good Food Gluten-Free* (Henry Doubleday Research Association, Bocking, Braintree, Essex).

ON COOKING WITH CHILDREN

Doreen Chetwood, *Young Cooks in the Kitchen* (Woodlands Craft Centre, Milton Ernest, Bedford MK44 1RF).

Cooking, Making Things to Eat (Practical Puffin).

Food Information Pack, National Centre for Alternative Technology, Machynlleth, Wales. (Booklets and posters on growing and producing food, diet, health, etc.)

ON GROWING YOUR OWN FOOD
Roy Genders, *Home-Grown Food* (Sphere).
Lawrence D. Hills, *Organic Gardening* (Penguin).

USEFUL ADDRESSES
Centre for Alternative Technology, Llwyngwern Quarry, Machynlleth, Powys, Wales. (Their list of *Useful Addresses* has a section on where to get wholefoods in the UK. Enclose a stamped addressed envelope.)

Foresight, Association for the promotion of preconceptual care, c/o Mrs Peter Barnes, Woodhurst, Hydestile, Godalming, Surrey GU8 4AY.

The Henry Doubleday Research Association, 20 Convent Lane, Bocking, Braintree, Essex (for advice on diet and organic gardening).

Hyperactive Children's Support Group, c/o Sally Bunday, 59 Meadowside, Angmering, Littlehampton, W. Sussex BN16 4BW. You can write for Dr Ben Feingold's (additive-free) diet for hyperactive children.

The Templegarth Club, 82 Tinkle Street, Grimoldby, Louth, Lincs LN11 8TF, produces interesting leaflets on diet, food and cultivating health generally.

The Vegan Society, 47 Highlands Road, Leatherhead, Surrey (for advice on vegan diet, which uses no animal products).

The Vegetarian Society, 53 Marloes Road, London W8.

Index